SHORT SEA SHIPPING 1997/98

—— by ——

Gilbert Mayes

and

Bernard McCall

INTRODUCTION

When we published *Short Sea Shipping 1995* we expressed the hope that updated versions would follow at regular intervals. That initial publication proved so successful that, two years on, we are able to offer this new edition which contains details of all Short Sea cargo vessels, owned, managed, chartered and agented by companies in the United Kingdom, and the Republic of Ireland. The most frequent request following the 1995 publication was that any future book should include details of the companies and ships engaged in the sea dredged sand and aggregate trade and this edition has been expanded to include these vessels.

As has often been said, shipowning in the 1990s is a complex business. It is sometimes almost impossible to know who precisely owns a vessel and therefore it is generally more convenient to speak about the "operator" of a vessel rather than the "owner". Within the company listings in the book, there are terms such as "managers for" and "agents for" and in using these terms we have followed the wishes of the operators and identified their involvement in the ships in the way they have requested.

In compiling this new edition, we are particularly grateful to all the operators for their willing assistance, encouragement and practical comments when answering the many queries necessary to ensure up to date information and accuracy. Without their support the book in this format would not be possible. Whilst we have endeavoured to check all details thoroughly we cannot accept any responsibility for errors or omissions, or their consequences. We hope that users will let us have their views on the usefulness of the book and its layout and would be grateful for pointing out any errors which may have appeared. Ship details are corrected to 31 December 1996 and all technical details are the latest available at the time of going to press.

The following information is given for each ship:

	Col 1	Col 2	Col 3	Col 4	Col 5	Col 6	Col 7	Col 8
SHIP NAME	Year	Gross	Deadwt	Length	Breadth	Draught	Service	Ship
(followed in brackets by	Built	Tonnage	Tonnage	(LOA)	Extreme	Loaded	Speed	Type
previous names and year								
of name change)								

Flag abbreviations comply with ISO 3166/1988

There are many others to whom we are grateful - to *Lloyd's Register of Shipping*; to those who have provided the photographs; to the many individuals who have passed information or answered a query; to the staff of Beacon Printers and last, but not least, to our families for their continued patience and support.

Gil Mayes   Bernard McCall
(Launcherley)   *(Portishead)*

ACOMARIT (U.K.) LTD.

28 Rutland Square, Edinburgh, EH1 2BU (0131 221 9441/fax 0131 221 9313)
Technical Managers for:
Liquid Gas Shipping Ltd

TARQUIN GLEN *(LBR)*	91	2985	3590	88,4	14,2	5,1	15	lpg
TARQUIN GROVE *(LBR)*	92	2985	3590	88,4	14,2	6,2	15	lpg
TARQUIN MARINER *(LBR)*	92	3693	4444	99,4	15,0	6,4	15	lpg
TARQUIN ROVER *(LBR)*	94	5821	5704	115,3	16,8	8,1	15	lpg
(Launched as Val Metavro)								
Tarquinius Compagnia di Navigazione								
TARQUIN NAVIGATOR *(LBR)*	95	5821	5632	115,3	16,8	7,0	15	lpg
Pentland Gas Carriers Ltd								
TARQUIN RANGER *(LBR)*	94	4317	5771	105,4	15,7	7,0	15	lpg
Tarquin Shipping Co S.A.								
TARQUIN TRADER *(LBR)*	88	3595	4320	98,3	15,0	6,6	15	lpg
New buildings (HHI-S. Korea)								
TARQUIN BRAE *(LBR)*	96	7300cum					15	lpg
TARQUIN MOOR *(LBR)*	early 97	7300cum					15	lpg

ADOHR ISLAND TRADING LTD.

Kilronan, Aran Islands, Co. Galway, Irish Rep.

NEWFYNE *(IRL)*	65	199	249	33,3	7,3	2,7	9	gen
(ex Glenfyne-88)								

C. F. AHRENKIEL SHIPMANAGEMENT (CYPRUS) LTD.

Omiros & Araouzos Tower, 25 Olympion Street, PO Box 3594, Limassol, Cyprus (+357 5 359731/
fax +357 5 359714)
Managers for:
C. F. Ahrenkiel (IoM) Ltd

MB ÁVON *(LBR)*	92	2373	4220	88,3	13,2	5,5	12	gen(96c)
MB CLYDE *(LBR)*	92	2373	4245	88,3	13,2	5,5	12	gen(96c)
MB HUMBER *(LBR)*	91	2373	4250	88,3	13,2	5,5	12	gen(96c)
MB THAMES *(LBR)*	92	2373	4250	88,3	13,2	5,5	12	gen(96c)

The **MB AVON** arrives in the Herdman Channel, Belfast *(Alan Geddes)*

ALDERNEY SHIPPING CO. LTD.

White Rock, St Peter Port, Guernsey, CI, GY1 2LN (01481 724810/fax 01481 724810) and 11 Victoria Street, Alderney, via Guernsey, CI (01481 822828/fax 01481 822065)
Agents only for:
Felix Shipping Ltd

ISIS *(IOM)*	78	674	953	57,5	10,1	3,4	11	gen(25c)
(ex Deer Sound-94, David Dorman-89)								
Unicorn Ltd								
LANCRESSE *(GBR)* +	78	674	953	57,5	10.1	3,4	11	gen
(ex Bressay Sound-94, Edgar Dorman-89)								

Note. + to be renamed

ALBA SHIPPING LTD. A/S

Gasvaerskvej 48, PO Box 636, 9100 Aalborg, Denmark, (+45 98 16 30 33/fax +45 98 16 16 33)

KASLA *(IOM)*	74	4724	6863	130,3	17,6	6,3	14	oil/ch tk
(ex Kiisla-96)								

ALEXANDERS PARTNERS (SHIPBROKING) LTD.

267 Cranbrook Road, Ilford, Essex, IG1 4TG (0181 518 3190/fax 0181 518 3009)
Chartering Managers/Agents for:
Arctic Wind Shipping Co Ltd

CERTAIN *(CYP)*	77	1104	1560	65,7	10,8	4,3	11	gen
(ex Concert Trader-94, Flevo-92. Plato-88, Flevo-81)								
Roca Shipping Ltd								
KISH *(BHS)*	78	1961	2973	84,2	13,9	5,4	14	gen
(ex Niewiadow-93, launched as Ran)								
Aniara Shipping Co Ltd								
ROMEO *(CYP)*	83	1908	3152	81,6	14,1	5,4	11	gen
(ex Andromeda-93)								

Note: Alexanders Partners *are also chartering managers/agents for vessels listed under other owners*

ALLANTONE SUPPLIES LTD.

139 Hamilton Road, Felixstowe, Suffolk, IP11 7BL (01394 670001)

CONVEYOR *(GBR)*	80	198	307	33,5	6,6	2,4	7	tk
ONWARD MARINER *(GBR)*	70	239	339	40,2	6,7	2,5	8	tk
Managers for:								
Southern Bunkering Ltd								
CONOCOAST *(GBR)*	68	209	330	35,3	7,6	2,7	8	tk
(ex Surehand-94, Bouncer-89)								
CONTRIBUTOR *(GBR)*	64	215	305	35,7	8,1	2,1	8	tk
(ex Conobay-96, Goodhand-95, BP Sprite-84, Torksey-76)								
General Port Services Ltd								
CONTRACTOR *(GBR)*	61	135	240	39,6	5,1	2,3	8	tk bge
(Conostream-96, Torfen, Blackmartin C)								
DELSTOR *(GBR)*	57	155	260	42,0	5,3	2,1	7	tk bge

Note: Allantone Supplies *is a wholly owned subsidiary of* GENERAL PORT SERVICES LTD.

AMBRA SHIPMANAGMENT LTD.

3 Makarios III Avenue, Mesa Yitonia, 4000 Limassol, Cyprus (+5 350469/ fax +5 352937)
Managers for:
Westermoor Shipping Co Ltd

| ZIM ESPANA (GBR) | 77 | 3807 | 4150 | 97,5 | 16,0 | 5,7 | 14 | gen(284c) |

(ex West Moor-95, Westermoor-86, Essex Courage-83, Westermoor-83)

ANEKTA MARINE LTD.

Gate 14, Gallions Point Marina, Woolwich Manor Way, London, E16 2PU (0171 511 7751/fax 0171 511 7750)

| LENNARD (GBR) | 1886 | 150 | 200 | 36,2 | 4,9 | 2,0 | 11 | bk tk bge |

ANGLO DUTCH MANAGEMENT SERVICES LTD.

PO Box 1, Woking, Surrey, GU22 0YL (01483 757563/fax 01483 757593)
Managers for:
Field Wave B.V.
RULEWAVE

| WARRIOR (BHS) | 78 | 1307 | 1426 | 84,9 | 9,5 | 3,3 | 10 | gen(69c) |

(ex Topaz-95, Aramon-94, Markab-86)

The ARCO DART photographed as she completes loading in the Bristol Channel　　　　　　(Dominic McCall)

ARC MARINE LTD.

Burnley Wharf, Marine Parade, Southampton, SO14 5JF (01703 634011/fax 01703 224068)

ARCO ADUR *(GBR)*	88	3498	5360	98,3	17,7	6,3	12	sd
ARCO DART *(GBR)*	90	1309	1700	68,1	13,0	4,1	10	sd
ARCO DEE *(GBR)*	90	1309	1812	67,7	13,0	4,1	10	sd
ARCO HUMBER *(GBR)*	72	5487	8962	107,0	20,1	7,4	14	sd
(ex Deepstone-86)								
ARCO SCHELDT *(GBR)*	72	1584	2928	76,5	14,3	4,9	12	sd
· (ex Amey III-73)								
ARCO SWALE *(GBR)*	70	1812	2928	80,6	14,3	5,1	13	sd
(ex Nabstone-86, Chichester Gem-79, Pen Stour-74)								
ARCO TEST *(GBR)*	71	594	835	63,6	9,9	3,3	10	sd
(ex Amey II-73)								
ARCO TRENT *(GBR)*	71	814	835	63,6	9,9	3,3	10	sd
(ex Amey I-74)								
Managers/operators of:								
Lombard Lessors Ltd								
ARCO ARUN *(GBR)*	87	3476	5360	98,3	17,5	6,3	12	sd
BMI (No.3) Ltd								
ARCO AVON *(GBR)*	86	3474	5360	98,3	17,5	6,3	12	sd
MCC Leasing (No.21) Ltd								
ARCO AXE *(GBR)*	89	3498	5348	98,3	17,7	6,3	12	sd
Consolidated Gold Fields PLC								
ARCO SEVERN *(GBR)*	74	1915	2806	81,5	14,1	5,0	12	sd
ARCO THAMES *(GBR)*	74	2929	4357	98,5	15,5	5,4	12	sd
ARCO TYNE *(GBR)*	75	2973	4357	98,5	15,5	5,4	13	sd
Civil & Marine Ltd								
CAMBECK *(GBR)*	89	3325	4745	99,6	17,0	6,3	12	sd
CAMBOURNE *(GBR)*	81	3249	4557	97,5	17,1	6,3	12	sd
CAMBRAE *(GBR)*	73	4107	5202	99,8	17,1	7,3	12	sd
CAMBROOK *(BHS)*	82	2318	3020	99,8	11,4	4,3	10	bulk
(ex Lena Wessels-87)								
Aggregate Industries Ltd								
CAMDIJK *(BHS)*	92	4960	9823	113,2	19,6	7,7	12	sd

ARGOMANN FERRY SERVICE GmbH

(Argo Reederei/Mann & Son London Ltd), Naval House, Kings Quay Street, Harwich, Essex, CO12 3JJ (01255 552744/fax 01255 240252)

Chartered tonnage:
Rederi AB Engship

GARDEN *(FIN)*	77	10762	7200	150,9	19,3	7,0	18	ro(115u)
(ex Liro Sun-93, Bore Sun-92)								

ARGOSEA MARINE LTD.

Isle of Man

ARGOSEA *(VCT)*	81	1774	2257	83,7	12,4	5,2	12	ref
(ex Emerald Aspen-94, Extrelago-88)								

ARKLOW SHIPPING LTD.

North Quay, Arklow, Co. Wicklow, Irish Republic (+353 402 39901/fax +353 402 32129)

Managers for:

Arklow Containers Ltd

ARKLOW CASTLE *(IRL)*	96	4984	6807	116,4	19,4	7,1	17	gen(549c)

Arklow Shipping (Overseas) Ltd

ARKLOW BAY *(IRL)*	88	1524	2169	73,9	11,8	4,4	10	gen(73c)
ARKLOW MANOR *(IRL)*	87	1524	2176	73,8	11,8	4,4	10	gen(73c)
ARKLOW MARSH *(IRL)*	88	1524	2171	73,8	11,8	4,4	10	gen(73c)
ARKLOW MEADOW *(IRL)*	90	1524	2160	73,8	11,6	4,4	10	gen(73c)
ARKLOW MILL *(IRL)*	88	1524	2166	73,8	11,8	4,4	10	gen(73c)
ARKLOW MOOR *(IRL)*	90	1524	2162	73,9	11,8	4,4	10	gen(73c)

Devon Line Ltd

ARKLOW BRIDGE *(IRL)*	96	4783	7182	99,9	17,2	6,8	12	bulk
ARKLOW BROOK *(IRL)*	95	4783	7182	100.0	17,2	6,8	12	bulk

James Tyrrell Ltd

ARKLOW SPIRIT *(IRL)*	95	2300	3211	89,9	12,6	4,7	11	gen(116c)
ARKLOW SPRAY *(IRL)*	96	2271	3211	89,9	12,6	4,7	11	gen(116c)
SHEVRELL *(IRL)*	81	1891	3033	83,8	12,6	5,0	10	gen

Invermore Shipping Ltd

ARKLOW VALE *(IRL)*	89	2867	4289	88,2	13,7	5,8	11	gen(173c)
ARKLOW VALLEY *(IRL)*	92	2827	4299	88,2	13,7	5,8	11	gen(173c)
ARKLOW VENTURE *(IRL)*	90	2827	4299	88,2	13,7	5,8	11	gen(173c)
ARKLOW VIEW *(IRL)*	91	2827	4299	88,2	13,7	5,8	11	gen(173c)
ARKLOW VIKING *(IRL)*	90	2827	4299	88,2	13,7	5,8	11	gen(173c)
ARKLOW VILLA *(IRL)*	91	2827	4299	88,3	13,7	5,8	11	gen(173c)

Coastal Shipping PLC

ARKLOW VALOUR *(IRL)*	90	2827	4299	88,2	13,7	5,8	11	gen(173c)
DUNKERQUE EXPRESS *(IRL)*	85	1839	2167	78,0	12,7	4,3	11	gen(124c)

(ex Inisheer-95, Lia Ventura-88, Flagship I-86, Elisa von Barssel-85)

INISHARK *(IRL)*	82	1895	3033	83,8	12,6	5,2	11	gen

(ex Darell-89)

INISHOWEN *(IRL)*	88	2749	3146	94,5	16,1	5,0	14	gen(262c)

(ex Angela Jurgens-96)

Fern Trading Ltd

EASTFERN *(IRL)*	81	1171	1644	70,6	10,8	4,3	10	gen

(ex Arklow Abbey-96)

The **ARKLOW BRIDGE**, a recent addition to the fleet of Arklow Shipping, makes steady progress along the Manchester Ship Canal *(Neil Burns)*

BALTIC FOREST LINE

PO Box 40, Manby Road, Immingham, Nth Lincolnshire, DN40 3EG (01469 571711/ fax 01469 571588)
Chartered tonnage:
Loften Shipping Ltd
LOFTEN *(ATG)*   75   1655   2140   75,7   11,9   4,7   12   gen(91c)
(ex Freja-96, Mosel-87)

BANKS SEAFARMS LTD.

Coel-na-Mara, St Margaret's Hope, Orkney, KW17 2TL (01856 831226)
LYRAWA BAY *(GBR)*   70   101   45   27,1   7,5   3,0   9   ro(2u)
(ex Sam-76)

BELFAST FREIGHT FERRIES LTD. (BFF)

Victoria Terminal 1, Dargan Road, Belfast, BT3 9LJ (01232 770112/fax 01232 781217)
SPHEROID *(IOM)*   71   7171   2838   124,2   19,2   5,0   19   ro(62u)
(ex Niekerk-87, RoRo Trader-85, Starmark-81)
Managers/operators for:
Lombard Corporate Finance
RIVER LUNE *(BHS)*   83   7765   5000   121,5   21,0   5,3   15   ro(80u)
(ex Stena Topper-93, Salar-93, Stena Topper-89, Bazias 7-89, Balder Vik-86)
Capital Leasing Ltd
SAGA MOON *(GIB)*   84   7746   2900   124,4   17,5   5,2   17   ro(62u)
(ex Lidartindur-86)
Chartered tonnage:
Rosal S.A.
MERLE *(BHS)*   84   9088   4734   120,0   21,0   5,3   15   ro(80u)
(ex Sally Euroroute-96, Bazias 3-93, Balder Sten-85)

Hurrying up the Bristol Channel to Avonmouth is the BELL ASTRON   *(Dominic McCall)*

BELL LINES LTD.

Bell House, Montague Street, Dublin 2, Irish Rep (+353 1 405 2696/fax +353 1 405 2686)

Chartered Tonnage:

Partenreederei m.s. "Amazone" Kahler & Sohne KG

AMAZONE *(DEU)*	87	2749	3178	94,5	16,1	5,0	14	gen(262c)

Unitas Schiffahrts mbH & Co. m.s. KG (Hermann Schepers)

BELL ADY *(ATG)*	95	2899	3950	99,3	16,2	4,9	14	gen(340c)

TESCH Bereederungsges mbH & Co. KG m.s. "Thea B"

BELL ASTRON *(DEU)*	95	2899	3850	99,3	16,2	4,9	14	gen(340c)

(launched as Thea B)

Swift Navigation Co Ltd

BELL ATLAS *(BMU)*	96	2906	3950	99,5	16,4	5,0	15	cc(340c)

Partenreederei m.s. "Bell Swift"

BELL SWIFT *(ATG)*	76	1599	3850	93,5	14,5	6,1	14	gen(205c)

(ex Jan-91, Arfell-90, Jan-87)

Partenreederei m.s. "Jan Becker" Bernd Becker KG

JAN BECKER *(DEU)*	87	2749	3173	94,5	16,2	5,0	14	gen(262c)

Partenreederei m.s. "Otto Becker"

OTTO BECKER *(DEU)*	89	2749	3144	94,5	16,1	5,0	14	gen(262c)

See also EURO CONTAINER SHIPPING

ALAN C. BENNETT & SONS LTD.

Lingley House, Commissioners Road, Strood, Rochester, Kent, ME2 4EE (01634 290780/fax 01634 290891)

TRACY BENNETT *(GBR)*	63	730	1210	55,5	11,3	4,4	9	sand

(ex David Marley-91)

BILBERRY SHIPPING & STEVEDORES LTD.

Bilberry, Waterford, Co Waterford, Irish Republic (+353 51 72224/fax +353 51 79372)

Managers for:

Sunwood Shipping Ltd

SAND MARTIN *(VCT)*	63	540	650	53,1	9,3	3,5	9	sd

(ex Sand Lark-91)

Sealsands Maritime Ltd

SEAL SANDS *(VCT)*	67	1535	2419	84,7	14,1	4,4	10	sd

(ex Zeeland-92, Stone Marshall-77, Needwood-73)

BP SHIPPING LTD.

Ship Management, BP House, Breakspear Way, Hemel Hempstead, Herts, HP2 4UL (01442 232323/ fax 01442 224102)

BRITISH TAMAR *(GBR)*	73	15163	25498	171,5	25,1	9,6	15	tk

Managers for:

BP Oil UK Ltd

BP BATTLER *(GBR)*	68	1410	2257	76,0	12,5	4,7	11	tk

(ex Inverness-76)

BP JOUSTER *(GBR)*	72	1568	2734	79,0	12,6	5,2	12	tk

(ex Swansea-76)

BP SPRINGER *(GBR)*	69	1071	1538	65,5	11,3	4,5	11	tk

(ex Dublin-76)

BP WARRIOR *(GBR)*	68	1410	2257	76,0	12,5	4,7	11	tk

(ex Grangemouth-76)

BRITANNIA SHIPPING LTD.

Brett House, Wincheap, Canterbury, Kent, CT1 3TZ (01227 829000/fax 01227 762601)
Managers for:
Natwest Leasing (GB) Ltd

BRITANNIA BEAVER *(GBR)*	91	3610	5786	100,0	17,7	6,2	12	sd

BRITISH DREDGING AGGREGATES LTD.

Avondale House, Avondale Road, Grangetown, Cardiff, CF1 7XB (01222 388666/fax 01222 226582)

BOWCROSS *(GBR)*	67	1006	1786	59,8	12,0	4,3	10	sd
(ex Chichester Cross-71)								
SAND TERN *(GBR)* *	64	561	801	53,0	9,3	3,5	9	sd

Managers for:
Filbuk III Ltd

WELSH PIPER *(GBR)*	87	1251	1923	69,0	12,5	4,4	11	sd

Note. * *Laid up Barry*

The **WELSH PIPER** passes Portishead on her way to discharge a cargo of sand at Avonmouth　　*(Dominic McCall)*

BULLAS TANKCRAFT CO. LTD.

Telegraph House, Telegraph Hill, Higham, Rochester, Kent, ME3 7MW (01634 717509/fax 01634 295079)

RAPID II *(GBR)*	71	801	1392	69,4	9,0	3,0	11	tk bge
(ex Celtic 4-94, Oiltrans 31-81)								
THAMES RAPID *(GBR)*	74	589	670	58,9	10,3	2,6	10	tk bge
(ex Rapid-86, BP Rapid-86, Sheppey-76)								

C. W. SHIPPING LTD.

Fountain Cross, Ennis, Co Clare, Irish Republic (+353 65 29124/fax +353 65 28316)

MATRISHA *(BHS)*	77	999	2250	79,2	12,4	4,8	12 gen (104c)
(ex Duisburg-88, Coburg-86, Boberg-84)							

Note.   Laid up damaged & condemned Ennis, Co Clare

CAMPBELL MARITIME LTD.

Maritime House, 6, Coronation Street, South Shields, Tyne & Wear, NE33 1LA (0191 427 0303/ fax 0191 455 0790)

Managers for:

Giles W. Pritchard-Gordon & Co Ltd								
ALICE P G *(BHS)* *	94	3627	6248	102,1	16,1	6,5	12	tk
LUCY P G *(BHS)* *	74	2527	3980	102,5	13,6	5,6	12	tk
(ex Corrie Broere-88)								
Franco British Chartering Agency Ltd								
ARDENT *(GBR)*	83	700	1180	50,0	9,5	3,6	9	gen
CORNET *(BHS)*	76	892	1255	64,0	10,5	3,8	11	gen(52c)
(ex Daunt Rock-88)								
MILLAC STAR II *(BHS)*	74	500	1535	75,7	11,8	3,9	12	gen
(ex Emanaich-86, Caravelle-83)								
ROUSTEL *(BHS)*	78	892	1240	64,0	10,5	3,7	11	gen(52c)
(ex Skellig Rock-88)								
TORRENT *(GBR)*	91	999	1733	63,6	11,0	4,1	9	gen
CASU Investments Ltd								
CAROLE T *(GBR)*	80	613	1120	49,6	9,5	3,9	9	gen
(ex Emily P G-93)								
Celtic Tankers PLC								
CELTIC TERRIER *(GBR)*	79	7676	12905	142,4	17,8	8,6	14	ch tk
(ex United Terrier-93, Ilse-91)								
Franco British Chartering Ltd & Singa Shipping Co Ltd								
DOWLAIS *(GBR)*	85	794	1394	58,3	9,4	3,9	8	gen
Eliza PG Ltd								
ELIZA P G *(BHS)* *	92	3338	5440	96,2	16,1	6,3	12	tk
Forth Tankers PLC								
FORTH BRIDGE *(GBR)*	92	3338	5800	96,2	16,1	6,6	12	tk
Pritchard-Gordon Tankers Ltd								
EMILY P G *(BHS)* *	96	3627	6150	102,1	16,1	6,5	12	tk
Newbuildings								
(3) (Appledore)	Jan 98		6250	102,1	16,1	6,5	12	tk
	Apr 98		6250	102,1	16,1	6,5	12	tk
	Jul 98		6250	102,1	16,1	6,5	12	tk

*Note: * Currently engaged in Caribbean trading*

The **FORTH BRIDGE** approaches Belfast's Victoria Channel   *(Alan Geddes)*

Carisbrooke Shipping's **CHERYL C** heads into the River Tees from Tees Dock *(Richard Potter)*

CARISBROOKE SHIPPING PLC

10 Mill Hill Road, Cowes, Isle of Wight, PO31 7EA (01983 284100 /fax 01983 290111)

CHERYL C *(BRB)*	83	1636	2367	70,1	13,1	5,0	10	gen(70c)
(ex Catarina Caldas-91, Catarina-89, Norbrit Rijn-87, Norbrit Hope-85)								
ELIZABETH C *(BRB)*	71	1768	2823	85,0	12,8	5,1	13	gen
(ex Mark C-96, Mark-86, Security-86)								
GRETA C *(BRB)*	74	1755	2628	77,8	13,2	5,0	12	gen
(ex Mairi Everard-90)								
HELEEN C *(BRB)*	74	1472	2159	71,3	11,6	5,0	12	gen
(ex Luther-89, Irina-81)								
MARY C *(BRB)*	77	1522	2440	66,1	13,1	5,1	12	gen
(ex Fiducia-89, Ligato-88)								
NATACHA C *(BRB)*	82	1636	2467	70,1	13,1	5,0	10	gen(70c)
(ex Natacha Caldas-91, Natacha-89, Norbrit Maas-87, Norbrit Faith-85)								
VANESSA C *(BRB)*	74	1853	3165	80,1	13,6	5,5	12	gen
(ex Vanessa-93)								

Managers for :
   Carisbrooke Shipping (196) Ltd (Carisbrooke Shipping/Scheepswerf Damen)

ANJA C *(BRB)*	91	2230	3222	99,7	12,6	4,3	10	gen(114c)
(ex Tima Saturn-92, launched as Union Saturn)								
NORDSTRAND *(BRB)*	91	1960	2800	88,3	12,5	4,6	11	gen(158c)
(ex Nicole-93)								

   Carisbrooke Short Sea Ltd

EMILY C *(BRB)*	96	2857	4650	89,8	13,2	6,0	11	gen(197c)

   Paneldeal Ltd

KLAZINA C *(BRB)*	83	1548	2554	81,3	12,0	4,3	10	gen
(ex Lasina-88, Klazina H-88, Klazina-85)								
MINKA C *(BRB)*	75	1655	2657	78,7	12,5	5,0	12	gen
(ex Victory-95)								
TINA C *(BRB)*	74	1458	2591	78,7	12,5	5,0	12	gen
(ex Vanda-95)								

   Mark C Shipping Ltd

MARK C *(BRB)*	96	2745	4619	89,8	13,2	6,0	11	gen(197c)

   Vectis Shipping Ltd

VECTIS FALCON *(BRB)*	78	2351	3564	87,0	13,8	5,7	12	gen
(ex Fribourg-93, Clarknes-83)								
VECTIS ISLE *(BRB)*	90	2230	3274	99,7	13,0	4,3	11	gen(114c)
(ex Lesley-Jane C-93, completed as Union Mercury)								

CLIFFGOLD LTD.

trading as N. E. MURRAY MARINE CONTRACTORS, 8 Rushenden Road, Queenborough, Kent, ME11 5BH
(01795 580998/fax 01795 665534)

SEACOMBE TRADER *(GBR)*	74	480	711	42,5	10,0	4,2	9	gen
SEALAND TRADER *(GBR)*	75	499	800	42,5	10,0	3,6	9	gen

(ex Island Swallow-96, Sealand Trader-87)
Managers for:
Sheridan Grange Ltd

CAPTION *(GBR)* *	63	189	269	32,1	7,2	2,3	8	sand

Bareboat charter:
Holyhead Towing Co Ltd

YEOMAN ROSE *(GBR)*	75	507	965	42,5	10,0	3,6	9	gen bge

(ex Island Swift-90, Seaborne Trader-87)
Note. * *Laid up at Queenborough*

COASTAL CONTAINER LINE LTD.

S.6 Berth, Royal Seaforth Container Terminal, Seaforth, Liverpool, L21 1JD
(0151 949-1000/fax 0151 949-10079)

Chartered tonnage:
Schiffahrtsgesellschaft J. Claussen KG
CHRISTOPHER

MEEDER *(ATG)*	76	2154	2200	86,9	13,0	4,8	13	gen(135c)

Kadueto Schiffahrt GmbH & Co KG m.s. "Liesel I"

COASTAL BAY *(ATG)*	91	2463	3269	87,4	13,0	5,1	12	gen(202c)

(ex Rhein Feeder-96, Rhein Lee-94, Rhein Feeder-93, Liesel I-91)
Astor Schiffahrtsges mbH & Co KG m.s. "Herm J"

HERM J *(ATG)*	90	2463	3200	87,4	13,1	5,1	12	gen(202c)

(ex Cari-Star-94, Primo-92, Medeur Primo-92, Rhein Carrier-91, Herm J-90)
Reederei Klaus Schneider KG

KIRSTEN *(ATG)*	83	2046	1876	78,0	13,9	5,0	13	gen(124c)

(ex Christopher Caribe-93, Saturnus-92, Craigavad-88)
KG m.s. "Neptunus" Reederei Kolb GmbH & Co

PELLWORM *(DEU)*	83	2046	1880	78,0	13,9	5,0	13	gen(124c)

(ex Neptunus-95, Craigantlet-88)

COLT INDUSTRIAL SERVICES LTD.

Colt Business Park, Witty Street, Hull, HU3 4TT (01482 214244/fax 01482 215037)

BUSTARDTHORPE *(GBR)*	14	77	98	28,0	5,2	2,0	7	gen bge
HUMBER MARINER *(GBR)*	63	103	300	42,1	5,3	2,1	8	tk bge
REBUS STONE *(GBR)*	63	165	275	35,1	6,6	2,1	7	tk bge

COMMODORE FERRIES (CI) LTD.

Commodore House, PO Box 10, Bulwer Avenue, St Sampson, Guernsey, C.I., GY1 3AF (01481 46841/
fax 01481 49543)

Time chartered:
NYDA Shipping L.P.
COMMODORE

GOODWILL *(BHS)*	96	11166	5238	126,4	21,4	6,0	17	ro(94u)

KS Nordic Shipping

ISLAND COMMODORE *(BHS)*	95	11166	5215	126,4	21,4	5,8	18	ro(94u)

CONTINENT IRELAND LINE

Maritime House, North Wall, Dublin 1, Irish Republic (+3531 874 1231/ fax +3531 872 5714)
Chartered tonnage:
Kapitan Manfred Draxl Schiffsbetriebs GmbH & Co KG m.s. "Gudrun"

| JANE *(ATG)* | 95 | 4628 | 5660 | 113,1 | 16,4 | 6,1 | 16 | cc(510c) |

(ex Gudrun-95)
Partenreederei m.s. "Partnership"

| YVETTE *(DEU)* | 96 | 6362 | 7225 | 121,4 | 18,5 | 6,7 | 16 | cc(700c) |

. (ex Partnership-96)

CORNISH CALCIFIED SEAWEED CO. LTD.

Newham Industrial Estate, Newham Road, Truro, Cornwall, TR1 2SU (01872 78878/ fax 01872 225555)

| DICTION *(GBR)* | 63 | 189 | 254 | 32,1 | 7,2 | 2,3 | 7 | sd |
| GOOLE STAR *(GBR)* | 70 | 210 | 375 | 33,5 | 6,6 | 2,7 | 7 | sd |

C. CRAWLEY LTD.

Town Pier, West Street, Gravesend, Kent, DA11 0BN (01474 365244 /fax 01474 320673)

| AQUATIC *(GBR)* | 63 | 199 | 315 | 35,1 | 7,5 | 2,3 | 7 | wt tk bge |

(ex Busby-85)

| AQUEDUCT *(GBR)* | 64 | 594 | 908 | 62,3 | 10,2 | 3,0 | 10 | tk |

(ex Charcrest-91)

| BRUCE STONE *(GBR)* | 64 | 357 | 375 | 43,7 | 9,2 | 2,3 | 8 | tk |

(ex Viaduct-78, Bruce Stone-76)

| FULFORD *(GBR)* | 60 | 477 | 522 | 50,3 | 10,2 | 2,6 | 10 | tk |

(ex Charmo-91)

| K/TOULSON *(GBR)* | 66 | 614 | 833 | 52,9 | 10,3 | 3,8 | 9 | tk |

(ex Beechcroft-90)

| MARPOL *(GBR)* | 57 | 200 | 360 | 36,6 | 6,5 | 2,6 | 8 | tk |

(ex Snydale H)

| PERFECTO *(GBR)* | 67 | 652 | 1008 | 59,2 | 10,7 | 3,2 | 9 | tk |

(ex Shell Driver-89, Perfecto-79)

| TOMMY *(GBR)* | 63 | 217 | 315 | 35,1 | 7,5 | 2,3 | 8 | tk |

(ex Batsman-87)

| TORDUCT *(GBR)* | 59 | 65 | 100 | 28,1 | 5,3 | 2,1 | 8 | tk bge |

(ex Wakefield-70)

The **K/TOULSON** photographed outward bound in the River Thames   *(Bernard McCall)*

CRESCENT SHIPPING LTD.

Hays House, Otterham Quay Lane, Rainham, Gillingham, Kent, ME8 7UN (01634 360077/fax 01634 387500)

AMBIENCE *(BHS)*	83	664	1020	59,6	9,3	3,2	9	gen
BANWELL *(GBR)*	80	1023	1710	71,9	11,1	3,7	10	tk
BLACKHEATH *(GBR)*	80	751	1230	60,0	11,3	3,4	11	tk
BOISTERENCE *(BHS)*	83	664	1020	59,6	9,3	3,2	10	gen
BRENTWOOD *(GBR)*	80	1004	1640	69,8	11,3	3,8	11	tk
CRESCENCE *(BHS)*	82	664	1020	59,6	9,3	3,2	10	gen
KINDRENCE *(BHS)*	76	2206	3210	91,2	13,5	5,1	10	gen
LUMINENCE *(BHS)*	77	1928	3210	91,3	13,5	5,1	10	gen
PIQUENCE *(BHS)*	79	1016	1452	72,5	11,3	3,3	10	gen
QUIESCENCE *(BHS)*	79	945	1452	72,3	11,3	3,3	10	gen
STRIDENCE *(BHS)*	83	1426	1821	84,7	11,5	3,4	10	gen
TARQUENCE *(BHS)*	80	664	1020	59,6	9,3	3,2	10	gen
TURBULENCE *(BHS)*	83	1426	1821	84,8	11,5	3,5	10	gen
URGENCE *(BHS)*	81	1425	1842	84,8	11,5	3,4	10	gen
VIBRENCE *(BHS)*	81	1425	1842	84,8	11,5	3,4	10	gen

Managers for:
Lloyds Leasing (North Sea Transport) Ltd

BARDSEY *(BHS)*	81	1144	1767	69,5	11,8	4,3	10	tk

(ex Sten-86)

BARMOUTH *(GBR)*	80	1144	1774	69,5	11,8	4,3	10	tk

(ex Per-86)
Lloyds Equipment Leasing Ltd

BLACKFRIARS *(GBR)*	85	992	1570	69,9	11,3	3,8	10	tk

Lloyds International Leasing Ltd

BLACKROCK *(GBR)*	89	1646	2675	78,5	12,7	4,9	10	tk

Lloyds Plant Leasing Ltd

BRABOURNE *(GBR)*	89	1646	2675	78,5	12,7	4,9	10	tk

Lloyds Industrial Leasing Ltd

BREAKSEA *(GBR)*	85	992	1570	69,9	11,3	3,8	10	tk

The **HOUNSLOW** makes her way back up the Thames from the dumping grounds   *(Bernard McCall)*

CRESCENT SHIP MANAGEMENT LTD.

Address and details as above

Managers for:

Cedar Yachting Ltd

ALEXANDER *(BHS)*	77	1788	3200	81,0	13,9	5,4	12	gen
(ex Veneto-95)								

Thames Water Utilities Ltd

BEXLEY *(GBR)*	66	2175	2471	89,9	15,1	4,1	12	sludge
HOUNSLOW *(GBR)*	68	2132	2471	89,9	15,2	4,1	12	sludge

Gansey Maritime

KRISTIANNE ELISA *(BHS)*	80	2465	3845	87,2	14,1	6,2	13	gen
(ex Maran-96, Uralar Cuarto-90)								

Don River Shipping Ltd

NANCY *(BHS)*	77	1788	3200	81,0	13,5	5,4	12	gen
(ex Blue Dream-94, Depatre-91, Centotre-88)								

City Leasing (Teeside) Ltd

THAMES *(GBR)*	77	2663	2936	93,3	15,1	4,6	12	sludge

CURRIE LINE LTD.

Tilly Flats, Lauriston Road, Grangemouth, Lothian, FK3 8XT (01324 483681/fax 01324 665018)

Agents for the following vessels on charter to Macvan B.V.:

Phoenix Reederei GmbH m.s. "Sirius P" KG

HIGHLAND *(ATG)*	90	2440	3181	87,5	13,0	4,8	12	gen(153c)
(ex Sirrah-95)								

Partenreederei m.s. "Scotland"

SCOTLAND *(ATG)*	74	1888	2340	76,7	13,2	5,2	13	gen(104c)
(ex Hornburg-95, Husum-85)								

DGW SAND CO.

Sandbank, 22 Sandyacres Road, Loggans, Hayle, Cornwall, TR27 5BA (01736 752961/fax 01736 757024)

COEDMOR *(GBR)*	46	181	244	32,9	6,1	2,6	7	sd
(ex Arran Monarch-64, Vic 57-48)								
SAND SNIPE *(GBR)* *	61	517	691	52,9	9,3	3,5	10	sd
SANDIE *(GBR)*	58	199	350	32,6	7,2	2,9	9	sd
(ex Sjobjorn VIII-90, Sandie, Wargon IV)								

*Note. * Laid up Hayle*

B.v. b. a. D. N. R. TANKVAART EN AGENTUREN

Kerkstraat 40, 4641 JT Ossendrecht, Netherlands (+31 0164 67 2121/fax +31 0164 67 2011)

Managers for:

Balata Ltd

GOLDCREST *(IOM)*	65	575	762	62,3	9,5	3,1	10	ch tk
(ex Silverkestrel-94, Goldcrest-92, Carrick Kestrel-87, Silverkestrel-75)								
SANDLARK *(IOM)*	66	688	952	57,0	9,8	4,4	11	ch tk
(ex Silverlark-94, Sandlark-92, Ice Lark-87, Finnlark-76)								

DALRIADA SHIPPING LTD.

Old Customs House, West Pier, Maritime Quarter, Swansea, West Glamorgan, SA1 1UN (01792 655300/fax 01792 642508)

BURE *(PAN)*	69	347	610	44,4	7,9	3,2	9	gen
(ex Cadence-85)								

DART LINE LTD.

Thames Europort, Dartford, Kent, DA2 6QA (01322 281122/fax 01322 281133)
John I Jacobs PLC

Name		Year							Type
DART 2	*(ROM)*	84	9080	4700	120,0	21,0	5,3	15	ro(80u)
(ex Bazias 2-95, Balder Hav-85)									

Chartered tonnage:
"C.N.M. ROMLINE" Shipping Co S.A.

Name		Year							Type
DART 5	*(ROM)*	86	9082	4700	120,0	21,0	5,3	15	ro(80u)
(ex Perseus-96, Bazias 5-95, launched as Balder Ra)									

JOANNA DAVIS

Norton Curlew Manor, Hatton, Warwick, CV35 8XQ (01926 842227/fax 01926 843314)

Name			Year						Type
EILEAN EISDEAL	*(GBR)*	*	44	96	138	20,3	5,6	2,0	7	gen
(ex Eldesa-84, VIC 72)									

*Note. * Laid up Island of Easdale*

DEAN'S TUGS & WORKBOATS LTD.

10 Wentworth Way, Hull, HU9 2AX (01482 219277/0860 301116)

Name		Year							Type
GEORGE ODEY	*(GBR)*	71	210	300	37,7	6,7	2,4	7	gen bge
HUMBER MONARCH	*(GBR)*	78	230	400	43,3	6,7	2,4	7	gen bge
JOLLY MINER	*(GBR)*	70	165	360	47,9	5,5	2,1	7	gen bge
MAUREEN ANN	*(GBR)*	62	207	380	34,4	6,6	2,4	8	gen bge
RISBY	*(GBR)*	68	186	300	39,6	5,5	2,1	8	gen bge

DEAN & DYBALL SHIPPING LTD.

Ocean House, Drivers Wharf, Princess Street, Northam, Southampton, SO14 0QD (01703 233366/ fax 01703 234246)

Name		Year							Type
DOUGLAS McWILLIAM	*(GBR)*	83	172	200	30,3	8,1	2,1	7	sludge
REEDNESS	*(GBR)*	68	900	1221	60,6	10,3	4,2	11	eff tk
(ex Kyndill II-86, Kyndill-85, Gerda Brodsgaard-73)									
TRENTAIRE	*(GBR)*	56	285	450	54,9	5,1	3,1	8	eff tk bge
(ex Languedoc-87)									
TRENTCAL	*(GBR)*	56	285	450	54,9	5,1	3,1	8	eff tk bge
(ex Auvergne-87)									

DENHOLM SHIP MANAGEMENT (I.O.M.) LTD.

PO Box 200, Circular Road, Douglas, IoM, IM99 1DH (01624 626582/fax 01624 624445)
Managers for:

Manx Car Carriers Ltd

Name		Year							Type
CITY OF BARCELONA	*(IOM)*	93	9576	2402	99,9	20,6	5,0	15	vc(806v)
CITY OF SUNDERLAND	*(IOM)*	93	9576	2417	99,9	20,6	5,0	16	vc(806v)

DENHOLM SHIP MANAGEMENT (U.K.) LTD.

The Parks, 107-115 Milton Street, Glasgow, G4 0DN (0141 353 1020/fax 0141 353 2366)
Managers for:

Arkansas Shipping Co

Name		Year							Type
SPANISH AYES	*(PAN)*	81	2971	4996	99,9	15,0	7,1	13	tk
(ex Ionian Eagle-96, Kobe II-93, Matsuyama Maru No. 21-92)									

DENVAL MARINE CONSULTANTS LTD.

156 High Street, Sevenoaks, Kent, TN13 1XE (01732 458288/fax 01732 458277)
Managers/agents for:
Larkspur Maritime Co Ltd

FLEUR-DE-LYS *(CYP)*	82	8553	5273	122,8	18,4	6,4	17	ro(105u)

(ex Lux Expressway-88, Roll Galicia-88)
Chartwell Navigation Co Ltd

ROSEANNE *(CYP)*	82	7744	4106	112,8	18,7	6,4	14	ro(80u)

(ex Faroy-89, Reina del Cantabrico-87, Salah Labiad-85, Reina del Cantabrico-83)

DOOLIN FERRY CO. LTD.

Doolin Pier, Doolin, Co Clare, Irish Republic (+353 65 74455)

PALBRO PRIDE *(IRL)*	64	200	367	41,6	7,7	2,3	8	gen

(ex Milligan-81, Lady Serena-77)

ONESIMUS DOREY (SHIPOWNERS) LTD.

La Salerie House, St Peter Port, PO Box 33, Guernsey, C.I.

The company is a wholly owned subsidiary of JAMES FISHER & SONS Public Limited Company . *See also* DUNDALK SHIPOWNERS, F. T. EVERARD, JAMES FISHER & SONS (LIVERPOOL), SWINSHIP MANAGEMENT and TORBULK.

DRAGON SHIPPING LINE

F Berth, King's Dock, Swansea, West Glamorgan, SA1 (01792 458854/fax 01792 456605)
Agents only for:
Bahamian Steamship Corp

KENMARE *(ATG)*	68	2435	2290	86,8	14,6	4,6	14	gen(88c)

(ex Kantone-87, Hermia-87, Marietta Bolten-74)

CORPORATION OF DUBLIN (Bardas Atha Cliath)

City Hall, Cork Hill, Dublin, Irish Republic
SIR JOSEPH

BAZALGETTE *(IRL)*	63	2258	2187	89,5	14,2	12,8	12	sludge

DUBLIN SHIPPING LTD.

6 Beechill, Clonskeagh, Dublin 4, Irish Republic (+3531 2691738/fax+3531 2839361)

RATHROWAN *(IRL)*	91	2920	4059	96,0	14,5	5,9	12	oil/ch/bit tk

Managers for:
Lynn Shipping Ltd

RATHCARRA *(IRL)*	88	6506	9939	119,8	19,0	8,0	12	oil/ch tk

(ex Vinjerac-95)
Kyle Shipping Ltd

RATHKYLE *(IRL)*	81	8162	14037	135,0	19,4	9,2	13	oil/ch tk

(ex Rich Star-87)
New building (Holland)

RATHBOYNE *(IRL)*	April 97		6600					oil/ch/bit tk

DUNDALK SHIPOWNERS LTD.

4 Jocelyn Court, Dundalk, Co Louth, Irish Republic (+353 42 39320/fax +353 42 26623)
Managers for:
Irish Continental Group PLC (IRISH FERRIES)
ROCKABILL *(IRL)*   84   3329   4115   98,7   15,5   5,4   14   gen(332c)
(ex Hasselwerder-94, Gracechurch Crown-90, Hasselwerder-89, City of Manchester-85, Hasselwerder-84)
Onesimus Dorey (Shipowners) Ltd demise chartered to Dundalk Shipowners Ltd
ROCKFLEET *(IRL)*   79   1000   1622   66,2   11,5   4,5   11   gen
(ex Globe-93)
ROCKISLAND *(IRL)*   78   492   1467   80,4   10,1   3,3   11   gen(47c)
(ex Verena-92)
SEA BOYNE *(IRL)* *   77   999   2192   79,1   12,4   4,8   12   gen(104c)
(ex Rockabill-93, Sybille-91, Echo Carrier-89, Scot Venture-88, Sybille-88)
Note.   * *Time chartered to* SEACON LTD *qv*

Photographed in the Humber approaching Grimsby is the SEA BOYNE   *(David H. Smith, courtesy ABP Grimsby)*

EAST OF SCOTLAND WATER

4 Marine Esplanade, Edinburgh, EH6 7LU (0131 553-9201/fax 0131 553-9269)
GARDYLOO *(GBR)*   76   1876   2695   85,9   14,2   4,7   12   sludge

EFFLUENTS SERVICES LTD. (ESL)

140 Moss Lane, Macclesfield, Cheshire, SK11 7YT (01625 429666/fax 01625 511305)
GREENDALE H *(GBR)*   62   311   536   43,1   6,7   3,1   7   sludge
HAWESWATER *(GBR)*   68   1469   1575   78,5   12,6   4,0   12   sludge
(ex Percy Dawson-88)

EURO CONTAINER SHIPPING PLC (ECS)

25 St Stephen's Green, Dublin 2, Irish Republic (+353 1 6610011/fax +353 1 6766090)
Managers for:
Taigro Ltd

BELL PIONEER *(IRL)*	90	6111	4833	114,5	18,9	5,9	14	cc(303c)
BELL RACER *(IRL)*	77	2213	3342	92,0	13,5	5,2	13	gen(168c)
BELL RULER *(IRL)*	77	2213	3342	92,0	13,5	5,2	13	gen(168c)
EURO POWER *(IRL)*	92	6455	5334	118,0	17,2	7,5	14	cc(378c)

(ex OOCL Shanghai-94, Euro Power-93)
See also BELL LINES

EUROPEAN CONTAINER SERVICES (EUCON)

Breakwater Road, Alexander Road, Dublin 2, Irish Republic (+353 1 8552222/fax +353 1 8552311)
Chartered tonnage:
Condra Schiffarts Gmbh & Co. KG m.s."Gertrud"

EMMA *(ATG)*	96	4628	5660	113,0	16,4	6,1	16	cc(510c)

(ex Gertrud-96)
Harren & Partner Schiffahrts GmbH

PAN TAU *(DEU)*	96	5544	7000	118,0	19,7	7,2	17	cc(600c)

S. EVANS & SONS

Ditton Road, Widnes, Cheshire, WA8 0NS (0151 424 3944/fax 0151 495 1571)

ST STEPHEN *(GBR)*	66	645	833	56,7	10,1	3,4	10	eff tk

(ex Kingsabbey-88, Rudi M-80, Teviot-79)
Note. Laid up Birkenhead and offered for sale

F. T. EVERARD & SONS LTD.

The Wharf, Greenhithe, Kent, DA9 9NW (01322 382345/fax 01322 383422)

ABILITY *(GBR)*	79	1696	2550	79,3	13,2	5,0	13	oil/veg tk
AUTHENTICITY *(GBR)*	79	1696	2550	79,3	13,2	4,9	12	oil/veg tk
SAGACITY *(BHS)*	73	1926	3238	91,3	13,3	5,1	12	gen
SPECIALITY *(BHS)*	77	2822	4245	89,7	14,3	6,0	12	gen(122c)
STABILITY *(BHS)*	78	2822	4245	91,1	14,3	6,4	12	gen(122c)

Managers for:
F. T. Everard Shipping Ltd

AGILITY *(GBR)*	90	1930	3144	80,0	14,6	5,6	11	tk
ALACRITY *(GBR)*	90	1930	3145	80,0	14,6	5,6	12	tk
AMITY *(BHS)*	80	1147	1767	69,5	11,8	4,3	11	tk

(ex Christian-88)

ANNUITY *(GBR)*	88	1711	3294	83,5	13,5	5,5	10	tk

(ex Janne Terkol-95)

APRICITY *(GBR)*	71	2144	3365	91,4	12,9	5,9	13	tk

(ex Petro Inverness-95, Esso Inverness-94)

ASSURITY *(GBR)*	71	2144	3349	91,4	12,9	5,9	13	tk

(ex Petro Penzance-95, Esso Penzance-94)

AVERITY *(BHS)*	81	1144	1770	69,5	11,8	4,3	11	tk

(ex Natalie-88)

SANGUITY *(GBR)*	84	1892	2887	79,0	12,7	5,1	10	gen(94c)
(ex Willonia-88)								
SOCIALITY *(GBR)*	86	1892	2887	79,0	12,8	5,1	10	gen(94c)
(ex Stevonia-87)								
New buildings (Sigmarine, Singapore)								
ASPERITY	early 97		3700				12	tk
AUDACITY	early 97		3700				12	tk
3i PLC								
AMENITY *(GBR)*	80	1696	2528	79,2	13,2	5,0	13	tk
PAMELA EVERARD *(GBR)*	84	1892	2887	79,0	12,7	5,1	10	gen(94c)
SELECTIVITY *(GBR)*	84	1892	2887	79,0	12,7	5,1	10	gen(94c)
Hadley Shipping Co Ltd								
COTINGA *(BHS)*	76	1921	3089	83,5	14,1	5,2	11	gen
Short Sea Europe PLC								
NORTH SEA TRADER *(GBR)*	91	2230	3222	99,7	12,5	4,3	11	gen(114c)
SHORT SEA TRADER *(GBR)*	91	2230	3263	99,7	12,5	4,3	10	gen(114c)
Scottish Navigation Co Ltd								
SENIORITY *(GBR)*	91	3493	5163	99,5	16,6	5,4	11	gen
SUPERIORITY *(GBR)*	91	2230	3212	100,0	12,5	4,3	11	gen(114c)

F. T. Everard's SENIORITY was designed to be one of the largest vessels capable of navigating the River Trent. She is seen in that river, heading for Grove Wharf to discharge a part-cargo of timber *(Richard Potter)*

F. T. EVERARD & SONS MANAGEMENT LTD.

4 Elder Street, London, E1 6DD (0171 247-8181/fax 0171 377-5562)

Freight managers for:

D. J. Goubert Shipping Ltd

CANDOURITY *(GBR)*	75	559	880	56,1	9,9	3,2	10	gen
Faversham Ships Ltd								
CONFORMITY *(GBR)*	75	559	880	56,1	9,9	3,2	11	gen

Onesimus Dorey (Shipowners) Ltd demise chartered to Torbulk Ltd, Grimsby

PENTLAND *(GBR)*	80	909	1315	60,0	11,3	3,9	12	gen
(ex Capacity-94, Lizzonia-89)								
PORTLAND *(GBR)*	80	909	1315	60,0	11,3	3,9	12	gen
(ex Comity-94, Angelonia-88)								

Note. F. T. Everard & Sons *are also freight managers/agents for vessels listed under other owners*

EXXTOR FERRIES LTD.

PO Box 40, Manby Road, Immingham, Nth Lincolnshire, DN40 3EG (01469 571711/fax 01469 571588)

ENDEAVOUR *(BHS)*	76	9963	5586	132,7	19,0	6,6	15	ro(95u)

(ex Bassro Star-95, Marcel C-89, Inger Express-81, Seaspeed Dora-78)

EXCALIBUR *(BHS)*	76	9737	5675	126,4	19,4	6,6	18	ro(95u)

(ex Stena Mariner-95, Senator-94, Salah L-93, Stena Mariner-90, Dana-83, Seaspeed Dana-81)

FALMOUTH OIL SERVICES (1994) LTD.

The Docks, Falmouth, Cornwall, TR11 4NJ (01326 311400/fax 01326 312989)

FALMOUTH								
ENDEAVOUR *(GBR)*	72	754	1276	62,7	9,8	4,2	11	bk tk

(ex Marwah II-87)

FALMOUTH								
ENTERPRISE *(GBR)*	72	1287	2189	76,0	11,2	5,1	11	bk tk

(ex Brady Maria-87, Hama Maru No 5-84)

Chartered tonnage:

John H. Whitaker (Tankers) Ltd

FALMOUTH								
ENDURANCE *(GBR)*	64	171	420	45,2	6,0	2,1	9	tk bge

(ex Humber Navigator-89)

FALMOUTH ENERGY *(GBR)*	63	165	275	42,1	5,3	2,1	7	tk bge

(ex Rufus Stone-89)

FALMOUTH INDUSTRY *(GBR)*	61	257	500	44,0	6,3	2,4	8	tk bge

(ex Ulster Industry-89)

W. FIELDGATE & SON LTD.

Haven Quay, Colchester, Essex, CO2 8JE (01206 865432 /fax 01206 866104)

Agents only for:

Seatrade Ltd

RAIDER *(VCT)*	66	224	378	41,6	7,7	2,3	8	gen

(ex Anglian Trader-90, Lee James-82, Target Venture-78, Sheena K-78, Lady Sheena-76)

FINBETA S.p.A.

Via Nazionale Piemonte 4, 17100, Savona, Italy (+019 822780/fax +019 823703)

ACQUAMARINA *(IOM)*	88	3533	6058	117,6	15,8	6,1	14	ch tk
CRISTALLO *(IOM)*	91	5038	8091	125,2	17,4	7,1	14	ch tk

FINN VALLEY OIL

Castlefinn, Co Donegal, Irish Republic (+353 74 46274)

FINN VALLEY OIL *(IRL)*	47	198	203	30,5	7,0	2,4	8	bk tk bge

(ex Sure Hand-89, Rinso-75)

JAMES FISHER & SONS PUBLIC LIMITED COMPANY

Fisher House, PO Box 4, Barrow-in-Furness, Cumbria, LA14 1HR (01229 822323/fax 01229 836761)

ECHOMAN *(GIB)*		82	3922	6125	104,3	16,7	6,8	12	oil/ch tk
FURNESS FISHER *(GBR)*		55	1721	2464	97,5	11,9	2,6	9	bk tk bge
(ex Nordicus One-89)									
NEW GENERATION *(GBR)*		66	2330	2233	86,7	16,5	4,6	11	ro h/l
(ex Kingsnorth Fisher-90)									
Managers for:									
James Fisher & Sons (Gibraltar) Ltd									
CABLEMAN *(GIB)*		80	4777	8496	117,2	17,5	7,2	12	tk
EASTGATE *(GIB)*		79	2072	3415	93,2	13,4	5,3	12	tk
IRISHGATE *(GIB)*		81	2071	3290	93,2	13,4	5,2	12	tk
NORTHGATE *(GIB)*		81	2071	3290	93,2	13,4	5,2	12	tk
OARSMAN *(GIB)*		80	1449	2547	76,1	12,5	4,9	10	tk
STELLAMAN *(GIB)*		80	2804	3680	97,8	13,8	5,8	12	ch tk
(ex Navajo-94, Richard-88)									
TANKERMAN *(GIB)*		83	5646	10716	119,7	19,2	8,1	11	tk
TILLERMAN *(GIB)*		75	7686	12800	142,5	17,8	8,6	12	tk
(ex Thuntank 2-89, Inga-83)									
WESTGATE *(GIB)*		79	2072	3368	93,2	13,6	5,3	12	tk
New buildings 4 (China)									
FORTH FISHER *(GBR)*		97	3150	3700				12	tk
(Launched as Quarterman)									
WHEELSMAN *(GBR)*	Apr	97	3000	3700				12	tk
	Jul	97	3000	3700				12	tk
	Nov	97	3000	3700				12	tk
Chartered tonnage:									
Anchorman Shipping Corp.									
ANCHORMAN *(LBR)*		93	4842	6417	101,6	17,5	6,9	12	tk
Chartsman Shipping Corp.									
CHARTSMAN *(LBR)*		93	4842	6417	101,6	17,5	6,9	12	tk
Rudderman Shipping Corp.									
RUDDERMAN *(LBR)*		94	4842	6417	101,6	17,5	6,9	12	tk
Steersman Shipping Corp.									
STEERSMAN *(LBR)*		94	4842	6403	101,6	17,5	6,9	12	tk
Managers for:									
British Nuclear Fuels Ltd									
EUROPEAN									
SHEARWATER *(GBR)*		81	2493	1583	80,0	12,6	5,1	11	nuc
(ex Mediterranean Shearwater-94)									

ONESIMUS DOREY (SHIPOWNERS) LTD and JAMES FISHER & SONS (LIVERPOOL) LTD *are wholly owned subsidiary companies.*

The **EUROPEAN SHEARWATER** arrives at Scrabster *(W. B. Mackay)*

JAMES FISHER & SONS (LIVERPOOL) LTD.

6th Floor, Martins Building, Water Street, Liverpool, L2 3UJ (0151 227-5531/fax 0151 236-2269)

BRIARTHORN *(GBR)*	80	1576	2435	74,6	12,9	4,9	12	gen
(ex Craigallian-89)								
DAVID M *(GBR)*	80	2077	3120	82,0	15,0	5,8	14	oil/ch tk
(ex BP Harrier-91)								
FREDERICK M *(GBR)*	80	1803	2924	75,2	13,3	5,8	12	ch tk
MICHAEL M *(GBR)*	80	2077	3120	82,0	15,0	5,8	14	tk
(ex BP Hunter-91)								
REDTHORN *(GBR)*	78	2025	3070	85,3	13,8	5,0	12	gen
(ex Pinewood-90)								
ROBERT M *(GBR)*	70	1675	2449	85,0	12,8	4,4	11	oil/bit tk
(ex Cree-77)								
ROSETHORN *(GBR)*	82	1213	1694	69.3	11,1	4,3	11	gen(60c)
(ex Shamrock Endeavour-90)								
SILVERTHORN *(GBR)*	82	1213	1694	69,3	11,1	4,3	11	gen(60c)
(ex Shamrock Enterprise-90)								
New building 2 (VSEL)	97		4500					tk

Managers for:
Onesimus Dorey (Shipowners) Ltd

SOLWAY FISHER *(IRL)*	77	1597	2703	73,3	13,2	5,1	11	gen(30c)
(ex Rockpoint-96, Arklow Valley-91, Procyon-84)								

The company is a wholly owned subsidiary of JAMES FISHER & SONS Public Limited Company *qv*

Making good progress in Southampton Water is the **REDTHORN** *(Chris Bancroft)*

KG FISSER & v. DOORNUM GmbH & CO.

Feldbrunnenstrasse 43-45, 20148 Hamburg, Germany (+49 040 44186241/fax +49 040 445686)

Agents only for:
Alsace Shipping Co Ltd

KELLS *(CYP)*	77	1986	2657	79,2	12,4	4,7	10	gen(104c)
(ex Gotaland-88)								
Kinsale Shipping Co Ltd								
KENMARE *(CYP)*	75	5306	8110	117,6	18,1	7,2	14	bulk
(ex Raute-86, Singapura-83, Raute-78)								

KINSALE *(CYP)* 76 5306 8150 117,6 18,1 7,3 15 bulk(170c)
(ex Rhombus-86, Wachau-84, Bayu-83, Rhombus-78)
Managers for:
Emerald Isle Bulkers Ltd
KILLARNEY *(IRL)* 77 2563 2908 96,3 12,4 4,8 12 gen(207c)
(ex Anholt-86, Neuwerk-81)
KYLEMORE *(IRL)* 77 2563 2908 96,3 12,4 4,7 12 gen(207c)
(ex Borssum-95, Bregenz-92, Bornholm-86, Neukloster-81)

FRODSHAM LIGHTERAGE CO.

9 Poulton Green Close, Spital, Bebington, Wirral, L63 9FC (0151 334 6715/fax 0151 334 6715)
Viaduct Shipping
PANARY *(GBR)* 37 167 260 29,5 6,5 2,6 8 gen bge
Humber & Hull River Lighterage
HULL PARAGON *(GBR)* 56 213 330 47,0 5,5 2,6 7 ed oil bge
(ex David W-96)

GAELIC SEAFOODS (IRELAND) LTD.

Dernish Island, Castletownbere, Co Cork, Irish Republic (+353 27 70376)
WILBERNIA 60 93 120 24,5 5,0 1,5 8 gen bge
(ex Cowes-72)

J. & A. GARDNER & CO. LTD.

16 Robertson Street, Glasgowm G2 8DU (0141 221-7845/fax 0141 204-2388)
SAINT BRANDAN *(GBR)* 76 1017 1394 63,8 10,8 4,1 10 gen/ro
SAINT KEARAN *(GBR)* 78 439 775 50,4 9,1 3,3 9 ch tk
SAINT ORAN *(GBR)* 81 621 719 53,3 9,2 3,4 10 gen/ro/ch
Managers for:
Golden Sea Produce Ltd
SOLEA *(GBR)* 89 235 326 33,5 7,6 3,4 9 fish
Knapdale Shipping (Campbeltown) Ltd (Lithgows Ltd/J & A Gardner & Co Ltd))
New building (C'beltown) Aug 97 35,0 8,6 4,0 9 fish

GENCHEM MARINE LTD.

Maritime House, 19A St Helens Street, Ipswich, Suffolk, IP4 1HE (01473 231121/fax 01473 232265)
Managers/agents for:
Parkside Warehousing & Transport
BORELLY *(GBR)* 71 571 905 55,7 9,9 3,3 10 gen
(ex Jana Weston-84)
James Wiseman
NAUTIC W *(VCT)* 71 470 646 49,4 8,8 3,1 9 gen
(ex Roy Clemo-86, Commodore Trader-81)

The **BORELLY** is seen in the Bristol Channel off Newport   *(Danny Lynch)*

GEORGE GIBSON & CO. LTD.

11 John's Place, Leith, Edinburgh, EH6 7EL (0131 554-4466/fax 0131 555-0310 & 554-0785)

Managers for:
    Lloyds Machinery Leasing Ltd

ETTRICK *(LBR)*	91	3023	3621	88,0	14,9	6,0	14	lpg
Lanrick Gas (Private) Ltd								
LANRICK *(LBR)*	92	3023	3621	88,0	14,9	6,0	14	lpg
Gas Shipping & Transport (Jersey) Ltd								
NORGAS TEVIOT *(LBR)*	89	7260	9259	132,2	18,0	8,6	17	lpg
(ex Teviot-96)								
TRAQUAIR *(LBR)*	82	5992	7230	113,8	18,4	8,1	16	lpg
Gibson Gas Tankers Ltd								
QUENTIN *(LBR)*	77	1709	2072	76,1	12,4	5,4	12	lpg
(ex Pentland Moor-79)								

G. T. GILLIE & BLAIR LTD.

178 New Bridge Street, Newcastle upon Tyne, NE1 2TE (0191 232-3431/fax 0191 232-8255)
Managers for:
    Starline Import Export Ltd

EILEAN DUBH E *(GBR)*	92	368	137	40,3	10,6	2,7	9	gen(17c)
(ex Sun Truck-94)								
Ensign Express Shipping Ltd								
RIVER DART *(GBR)*	81	536	825	50,0	9,3	3,4	10	gen

Note. Gillie & Blair *are commercial managers for other dry cargo vessels*

T. E. GRACE

(West Country Sand & Gravel), Rolle Quay, Barnstaple, N. Devon EX32 8JE (01271 45842/fax 01271 831029)

DEERHURST *(GBR)*		33	158	200	30,6	6,6	2,4	7	gen bge
TED GRACE *(GBR)* *		49	113	202	30,6	5,4	2,4	8	sd
(ex Sand Pearl-80, Wycliffe-70)									
MARLENE GRACE		66	62	76	18,3	5,5	2,3	11	sand
(ex Pen . . , Marley)									
West Country Sand & Gravel									
BUSY GRACE *(GBR)* *		63	50	60	15,8	3,7	1,5	8	sand
(ex Busy Bee-89)									
LOUISA GRACE *(GBR)*		60	50	65	15,8	4,8	1,9	8	sand
(ex RH 13-79)									

*Note: * Laid up Barnstaple*

GRACECHURCH LINE LTD.

2nd Floor, Port of Liverpool Buildings, Pier Head, Liverpool, L21 1BZ (0151 231-1144/fax 0151 231 1375)

Chartered tonnage:
Herman Buss KG m.s. "Western Trader"

GRACECHURCH METEOR *(ATG)*		91	4164	4750	111,1	16,1	6,0	14	gen(381c)
(Completed as Western Trader)									

Reederei m.s. "Gerdia" Heinz Freese K.G.

GRACECHURCH STAR *(DEU)*		94	5026	6449	117,0	18,2	6,9	16	gen(538c)
(ex Gerdia-96, Alum Bay-96, Gerdia-94)									

Reedereiges m.s. "Komet" Henry Gerdau KG GmbH & Co

GRACECHURCH PLANET *(DEU)*		94	4984	7014	116,4	19,5	7,1	16	gen(532c)
(ex Planet V-96)									

Partenreederei m.s. "Katherine Borchard"

KATHERINE BORCHARD *(ATG)*		79	5378	7283	126,3	18,1	6,5	15	gen(462c)
(ex Concordia-86, Katherine Borchard-86, Concordia-85, Zim Australia-82, launched as Concordia)									

Note. See also CHARLES M. WILLIE & CO (SHIPPING) for other chartered tonnage

GROVEFIELD FINANCE LTD.

Ipswich

CARMEL *(HND)* *		71	199	411	41,8	7,7	2,7	9	gen
(ex Valour-93, Subro Valour-91, Ferryhill II-78)									

*Note. * Laid up Colchester*

HAGGERSTONE MARINE LTD.

2A Fanshawe Crescent, Hornchurch, Essex, RM11 2DD (01708 458695/fax 01708 477349)

Managers for:
Balena Marine Ltd

DORIS I *(PAN)*		64	737	877	64,8	9,9	3,5	10	ed oil tk
(ex Doris-81)									

The **DORIS** 1 seen outward bound in the New Waterway *(Dominic McCall)*

HALCYON SHIPPING LTD.

Europa House, 40 South Quay, Gt Yarmouth, Norfolk, NR30 2RL (01493 856831/fax 01493 857533) (also at 19 London Road North, Lowestoft, Suffolk)

Agents only for:

Whiting (Shipping) Ltd

BRENDONIAN *(GBR)*	66	587	837	54,0	9,1	3,6	10	gen
(ex Brendonia-84)								

Tara Shipping Ltd

ELLEN W *(VCT)*	74	459	645	47,8	8,8	3,1	9	gen
(ex Guy Chipperfield-82)								

Herbert Trading Ltd

REMA *(HND)*	76	748	1041	63,0	9,5	3,1	10	gen
(ex Fivel-95, Pergo-87)								

HAY & CO. (LERWICK) LTD.

66 Commercial Street, Lerwick, Shetland, ZE1 0JD (01595 692533/fax 01595 692781)

Managers for:

John Fleming & Co Ltd

SHETLAND TRADER *(GBR)*	72	847	1133	60,9	10,2	3,9	12	gen(36c)
(ex Parkesgate-79)								

HENTY OIL LTD.

No. 1 Huskisson Dock, Liverpool, L3 0AT (0151 922 0622/fax 0151 922 0626)

TAFFGARTH *(GBR)*	50	161	236	37,0	5,9	2,1	7	bk tk bge
(ex Contractor-85, Regent Wren-71)								
WHEATCROFT *(GBR)*	57	189	300	42,8	5,5	2,1	7	bk tk bge

PETER M. HERBERT

Bideford, N. Devon

JOHN ADAMS *(GBR)* *	34	94	165	26,0	6,0	2,8	7	gen

Note. * *Laid up Bideford (East-the-Water)*

TANKSKIBSREDERIET HERNING A/S
(HERNING SHIPPING A/S)

Utzonhuset, Olufsvaenget 29, 7400 Herning, Denmark (+ 45 97126777/fax +45 97 127279)

Managers for:
I/S Ditte Theresa

DITTE THERESA *(IOM)*	77	2813	4501	92,8	14,7	6,8	13	ch tk
(ex Bravado-96)								

I/S Herning Chemical Tankers

GRETE THERESA *(IOM)*	68	772	1061	64,0	9,9	3,9	11	oil/ch tk
(ex Unicorn Michael-91, Onabi-77)								

HIGHLAND MARINE LTD.

Railway Pier, Kyle of Lochalsh, Ross-shire, IV40 8AL (01599 534820/fax 01599 534865)

SALINA *(GBR)*	62	212	371	35,4	7,5	3,2	9	gen
(ex Karla-92, Mebeto-71, Tommelise-65)								

Managers for:
Roderick Cunningham (Scalpay) Ltd

ISLE OF TIREE *(GBR)*	61	131	78	29,0	7,1	2,7	11	gen
(ex Ocean Hunter (A 197)-74, Caledonian (A 197)-71)								

HOLYMANSALLY FERRIES

Argyle House, York Street, Ramsgate, Kent, CT11 9DS (01843 595566/fax 01843 593454)

Chartered tonnage:
Channel Island Ferries Ltd

PURBECK *(BHS)*	78	6507	1550	125,5	17,5	4,5	18	ro(52u)

Rosal S. A.

SALLY EUROLINK *(BHS)*	85	9088	4734	120,0	21,0	5,3	14	ro(80u)
(ex Bazias 4-93, Balder Bre-85)								

Landi Shipping Co Ltd

SALLY EUROWAY *(CYP)*	76	9079	5485	127,0	19,9	6,5	19	ro(94u)
(ex Saga Aries-95, Aries-94, Norcove-94, Argo-91, Argo-Hellas-80, Brabant-78, Argo-77)								

The **PICASSO** moves cautiously astern towards her berth at Immingham *(Barry Standerline)*

HOVERSPEED & FALCON SEA FREIGHT LTD.

Freight Office, Folkestone Harbour, Folkestone, Kent, CT20 1QH (01303 221456/fax 01303 248709)
Chartered tonnage:
Vessel Holdings 3 Ltd
PICASSO *(CYM)*   77   5669   2840   115,1   17,5   5,3   17   ro(65u)
(ex Poker-95, Beaverdale-91, Wuppertal-87, Canaima-79, Wuppertal-78)

D. V. HOWELLS (DVH)

Milford Docks, Milford Haven, Pembrokeshire, SA73 3AF (01646 692418/ fax 01646 690179)
HELMSDALE *(GBR)*   55   110   200   26,9   5,9   2,1   7   bk tk bge
(ex Helmsdale H)
WIKNER *(GBR)*   50   87   110   21,1   6,6   2,1   6   gen bge
(ex S.A. Wikner)

HUELIN-RENOUF SHIPPING SERVICES

PO Box 17, New North Quay, St Helier, Jersey, CI (01534 610345/fax 01534 610346)
Managers for:
Aubreyville Ltd
HUELIN DISPATCH *(BHS)*   78   1892   2360   79,8   12,8   4,5   12   gen(104c)
(ex Stenholm-96, Visbur-92, Stenholm-91, Suderelv-91)

INTERNATIONAL CHARTERING PLC

15 Gloster Road, Martlesham Heath, Ipswich, Suffolk, IP5 7RJ (01473 626646/fax 01473 610256)
SWIFT TRADER *(IOM)*   77   1899   2621   79,8   13,2   5,2   12   gen
(ex Swift-85)

INTERNATIONAL CHEMICAL TRANSPORT BELGIUM NV (I.C.T.B.)

Frilingei 173, 2930 Brasschaat, Belgium (+32 03 605 29 81/fax +32 03 605 29 78)
Managers for:
Longshore Maritime Inc
ARCTICA *(IOM)*   69   2671   4232   98,9   12,5   6,4   12   asp tk
(ex Arctic 1-94, Otelia-88)
Toridon Holdings
OSPREY *(VCT)*   73   2612   4082   101,0   14,1   6,6   13   oil/ch tk
(ex Sandgrouse-96, Latex-89, Ferton-84, Xileno-79)

INTERNATIONAL SHIPBROKERS LTD.

7 Crescent, London EC3N 2LY (0171 680 0068/fax 0171 680 9702)
Chartered tonnage:
Rederij Harma
HARMA *(NLD)*   79   999   1455   65,0   10,7   4,0   10   gen
B.V. Zeelichter "Thames II"
WILHELMINA V *(NLD)*   75   959   1450   65,0   10,8   4,1   11   gen

INTERSEA OPERATIONS LTD. INC.

PO Box 7560, 3000 HN Rotterdam, Netherlands (+31 0181 240 3403/fax +31 0181 355535)
Managers for:
Chesham Containers Ltd

AMERSHAM *(GBR)*	80	6764	9663	120,8	20,9	7,9	14	cc(528c)
(ex Panarea I-96)								
CHESHAM *(GBR)*	80	6764	9809	120,8	20,9	7,9	14	cc(528c)
(ex Oahu-96)								

INTRADA CHARTERING LTD.

75 Main Road, Gidea Park, Romford, Essex , RM2 5EL (01708 739-353/fax 01708 739-252)
Managers for the following vessels on charter to Scotline Ltd:
Wolfgang & Carsten Kleige

CHARLOTTE *(ATG)*	69	1440	1477	77,2	11,8	4,0	11	gen(72c)
(ex Hinrich Behrmann-89, Tweed-70, Launched as Hinrich Behrmann)								
Hohebank Shipping Ltd								
HOHEBANK *(BHS)*	78	1687	1600	79,7	12,8	3,7	11	gen(82c)
Jan Peter Ludtke KG								
INGA *(DEU)*	85	1584	1783	82,0	11,5	3,5	10	gen
Partenreederei m.s. "Konigsburg"								
KORALLE *(ATG)*	85	1851	2269	80,0	12,7	4,2	10	gen(142c)
(ex RMS Hollandia-94, Koralle-92)								
Heinz Litmeyer Schiffahrts K.G. m.s. "Emsland"								
EMSLAND *(ATG)*	84	1857	2200	80,2	12,7	4,2	11	gen(102c)
Scot Trader Shipping Ltd								
SCOT TRADER *(BHS)*	86	1584	1900	82,0	11,5	3,7	10	gen
(ex Wotan-93, Scot Trader-91, Wotan-86)								
Scot Ranger Shipping Ltd								
New building (YDD)								
SCOT RANGER *(BHS)*	Feb. 97	2250	3360	84,9	12,6	5,1	11	gen

The **HOHEBANK** makes steady progress through the North Sea with a full cargo of timber from Sweden *(Richard Jones)*

ISLE OF MAN STEAM PACKET CO. LTD.

Imperial Buildings, PO Box 5, Bath Place, Douglas, IoM, IM99 1AE (01624 623344/fax01624 645609)

BELARD *(IOM)*	79	5801	3480	105,6	18,8	5,0	16	ro(50u)

(ex Mercandian Carrier II-85, Carrier II-85, Mercandian Carrier II-84, Alianza-83, Mercandian Carrier II-83)

PEVERIL *(IOM)*	71	5254	1685	106,3	16,0	5,0	14	ro(45u)

(ex N. F. Jaguar-82, Penda-80, ASD Meteor-75, Holmia-73)

ISLE OF SCILLY STEAMSHIP CO. LTD.

Hugh Town, St Mary's, PO Box 10, Isles of Scilly (01720 422357/fax 01720 422192) & Quay Street, Penzance, TR18 4BD (01736 62009 /fax 01736 51223)

GRY MARITHA *(GBR)*	81	590	528	40,3	9,8	3,7	9	gen/pt

JEBSEN SHIP MANAGEMENT (LONDON) LTD.

Jebsen House, 53-55 High Street, Ruislip, Middx, HA4 7AZ (01895 676341/fax 01895 675729)

Managers for:

Geralia Shipping Co Ltd

HERNES *(CYP)*	80	4924	7106	110,6	17,6	7,0	12	gen

(ex Rora Head-93)

Viscaya Shipping Inc

HORDNES *(PAN)*	80	4913	7107	110,6	17,6	7,0	12	gen

(ex Barra Head-96)

HUSNES *(PAN)*	77	4907	7174	110,6	17,6	7,0	15	gen

(ex Hook Head-93, Sumburgh Head-90)

Jebsens Thun Beltships Investments Ltd

TELNES *(PAN)*	82	6944	10110	117,7	20,6	8,5	14	bulk
TINNES *(NIS)*	83	6944	10110	117,7	20,6	8,5	14	bulk

(ex General Bonifacio-88, Tinnes-86)

Powergen Plc

LORD CITRINE *(GBR)*	86	14201	22447	154,9	24,5	9,0	12	bulk
LORD HINTON *(GBR)*	86	14201	22447	154,9	24,5	9,0	12	bulk

SIR CHARLES

PARSONS *(GBR)*	85	14201	22530	154,9	24,5	9,0	12	bulk

Altnamara Shipping PLC

RADNES *(GBR)*	76	3885	6258	103,6	16,0	7,0	13	bulk

(ex Lugano-89, Radnes-84)

The **HOO KESTREL**, outward bound in the River Ouse, passes Reedness   *(Barry Standerline)*

R. LAPTHORN & CO. LTD.

Buttercrock Wharf, Vicarage Lane, Hoo, Rochester, Kent, ME3 9LQ (01634 250369/fax 01634 250759)

ANNA MERYL *(GBR)*	91	999	1704	69,1	9,9	3,9	9	gen
(ex Anna Maria-94)								
HOOCREEK *(GBR)*	82	671	1236	50,0	9,4	4,1	8	gen
HOO VENTURE *(GBR)*	82	671	1180	50,0	9,5	4,0	8	gen

Managers for:
R. Lapthorn Shipping Ltd

HOO BEECH *(GBR)*	89	794	1399	58,3	9,5	3,6	9	gen
HOO DOLPHIN *(GBR)*	86	794	1412	58,3	9,6	3,9	9	gen
HOO LARCH *(GBR)*	92	1382	2225	77,8	11,1	4,0	10	gen
HOO LAUREL *(GBR)*	84	794	1394	58,3	9,5	3,9	8	gen
HOO MAPLE *(GBR)*	89	794	1399	58,3	9,5	3,9	9	gen
HOO MARLIN *(GBR)*	86	794	1412	58,3	9,5	3,9	8	gen
HOO PLOVER *(GBR)*	83	671	1234	50,0	9,5	4,0	8	gen
HOO ROBIN *(GBR)*	89	794	1400	58,3	9,5	3,9	9	gen
HOO TERN *(GBR)*	85	794	1394	58,3	9,5	3,9	8	gen
HOO WILLOW *(GBR)*	84	671	1234	50,0	9,5	4,0	8	gen
HOOCREST *(GBR)*	86	794	1400	58,3	9,6	3,9	9	gen
HOOPRIDE *(GBR)*	84	794	1394	58,3	9,5	3,9	8	gen

R. Lapthorn & Co Ltd & R. Lapthorn Shipping Ltd

HOO FALCON *(GBR)*	91	1382	2225	77,8	11,1	4,0	9	gen
HOO FINCH *(GBR)*	89	794	1377	58,3	9,5	3,9	9	gen
HOO KESTREL *(GBR)*	93	1382	2225	77,8	11,1	4,0	10	gen
HOO SWAN *(GBR)*	86	794	1412	58,3	9,5	3,9	8	gen
HOO SWIFT *(GBR)*	89	794	1399	58,3	9,5	3,9	9	gen

Harris & Dixon (Shipbrokers) Ltd

ILONA G *(GBR)*	90	999	1700	69,1	10,8	3,9	10	gen

John H. Whitaker (Holdings) Ltd & Bayford & Co Ltd

BETTY-JEAN *(GBR)*	85	794	1360	58,3	9,5	3,9	8	gen
FAST KEN *(GBR)*	92	1382	2220	77,8	11,1	4,0	9	gen
(ex Bowcliffe-94)								

FREDERICK CHARLES LARKHAM & SONS LTD.

Severn Mill, The Strand, Westbury-on-Severn, Glos, GL14 1PG (01452 760368/fax 01452 760368)

BACCARAT *(GBR)*	59	293	325	45,7	8,7	2,2	8	tk bge/gen
BOXER *(GBR)*	65	197	315	35,1	7,6	2,0	8	gen bge
HOOK SAND *(GBR)* +	64	186	280	35,4	7,2	2,7	7	sd
(ex Polo III-81, Amanda-75)								

Note. + *Also engaged in maintenance dredging*

WALTHER LASS

Grosse Elbstrasse 36, Hamburg-Altona, 22767, Hamburg, Germany (+49 040 3196088 /fax +49 040 3196956)

Agents only for:
Northumbria Shipping Ltd

NORTHUMBRIA LASS *(HND)*	68	498	895	59,1	9,9	3,6	11	gen
(ex Mary H-89, Northumbria Lass-87, Fencer Hill-79, Stevnsnaes-77)								

Hammann and Prahm's REBECCA HAMMANN heads up the River Trent, bound for Flixborough   *(David H. Smith)*

LEAFE & HAWKES LTD.

Merrick Street, Hedon Road, Hull, HU9 1NF (01482 325951/fax 01482 225406)
Time chartered tonnage:

Hammann & Prahm Reedereiges mbH & Co. KG m.s. "Eric Hammann"

ERIC HAMMANN *(DEU)*	91	1156	1323	58,8	11,7	3,6	9	gen(50c)
EVERT PRAHM *(DEU)*	96	1598	2420	76,4	12,7	4,5	10	gen

Hammann & Prahm Bereederungsges mbH & Co KG m.s. "Gerhard Prahm"

GERHARD PRAHM *(DEU)*	82	1022	1089	74,5	9,5	2,9	10	gen
(ex RMS Bavaria-96, Gerhard Prahm-92)								

Hammann & Prahm Reederei GmbH & Co. KG m.s. "Heyo Prahm"

HEYO PRAHM *(DEU)*	87	1156	1323	58,0	11,7	3,5	10	gen(50c)

Hammann & Prahm GmbH & Co.KG

LORE PRAHM *(DEU)*	89	1156	1323	58,0	11,8	3,6	9	gen(50c)
WALTER HAMMANN *(DEU)*	88	1156	1323	58,8	11,7	3,5	9	gen(50c)

Hammann & Prahm Bereererungsges mbH & Co KG m.s. "Martha Hammann"

MARTHA HAMMANN *(DEU)*	85	1832	2287	80,7	12,7	4,2	11	gen(112c)

Reederei Hammann & Prahm GmbH & Co KG m.s. "Rebecca Hammann"

REBECCA HAMMANN *(DEU)*	95	1595	2350	76,4	12,7	4,5	10	gen

Hammann & Prahm Bereederungsges mbH & Co KG m.s "Sheila Hammann"

SHEILA HAMMANN *(DEU)*	83	1022	1113	74,5	9,5	2,9	10	gen
(ex RMS Anglia-96, Sheila Hammann-92)								

Hammann & Prahm Reedereiges mbH & Co. m.s. "Selene Prahm"

SELENE PRAHM *(DEU)*	94	1584	2422	75,1	12,7	4,5	10	gen

m.s. "Wilhelmine Steffens" Reederei Steffens GmbH & Co

WILHELMINE STEFFENS *(DEU)*	81	1022	1092	74,3	9,5	2,9	10	gen
(ex RMS Scotia-96, Wilhelmine Steffens-92, Lucky Star-91)								

The **DICTION** is seen in tranquil conditions near Truro.   *(Tony Atkinson)*

By contrast, the **SHETLAND TRADER** makes stately progress as she heads south in the North Sea, east of Peterhead.   *(Richard Jones)*

The **LADY REA**, operated by Thomas Watson (Shipping) Ltd., hurries up the New Waterway and passes the Hook of Holland on her way to Rotterdam. *(B. T. Plues)*

The **TORRENT** is photographed on the River Neath, having loaded at Briton Ferry. *(Bill Moore)*

As she heads up the Bristol Channel to Avonmouth, the **MICHAEL M** sports the attractive and distinctive colours of Metcalf Motor Coasters, although she has been owned by larger groups which succeeded the Metcalf company. *(Bernard McCall)*

The **WHITHAVEN** passes Portishead on her way from Avonmouth to load a further cargo of bunker fuel at Milford Haven. *(Bernard McCall)*

A regular visitor to Selby, the **NAUTIC W** heads down the river Ouse after discharging cargo at that port.
(Barry Standerline)

The **SWANLAND** is a recent addition to the fleet operated by Torbulk Ltd. She is seen arriving at Sinclair Wharf, Belfast.
(Alan Geddes)

The BLACKBIRD is seen outward bound in the River Bann with a cargo of scrap from Coleraine *(Stephen Woods)*

LIBRA SHIPPING B.V.

Maaskade 159A, 3071 NR Rotterdam, Netherlands (+31 010 4117740/fax +31 010 4117769)
Agents only for:
Primula Ltd

BLACKBIRD *(VCT)*	67	1197	1735	75,8	11,2	4,4	12	gen

(ex Hawthorn-92, Francinaplein-77, Hunnau-73, Ortrud Muller-69)

BLUEBIRD *(BHS)*	82	1115	1688	67,4	11,3	4,1	10	gen(54c)

(ex Alice-95, Alila-92, Peacock Venture-88)
Cormorant Shipping & Trading Ltd

EGRET *(VCT)*	66	633	738	57,4	9,1	2,8	9	gen

(ex Cormorant-86, Moon Trader-86, A. Held-79)

LLANELLI SAND DREDGING LTD.

Windmill Park, Burry Port, Dyfed (01554 832475)
Chartered tonnage:
Baggermaatschappij Boskalis B.V.

SOSPAN *(PAN)* +	90	718	1300	57,0	10,0	3,6	7	drg/hpr

Note: + *Also employed on maintenance & capital dredging in EU waters. The company is part of the* Royal Boskalis Westminster Group

LOGANTOR LTD.

trading as MERSEY TANKER LIGHTERAGE, 17 Owarside Drive, Wallasey, Wirral, Merseyside L45 5HZ
(0151 638 3813)

SAFE HAND *(GBR)*	50	205	203	30,6	7,0	2,4	8	tk bge

(ex Lux-75)

MARIMED AGENCIES (UK) LTD.

27 Fishers Lane, London, W4 1RX (0181 742-3535/fax 0181 742-3394)
Managers for :
Ballard Maritime Inc
ANAIS *(BHS)*   85   3402   3073   93,8   16,3   6,0   12   ref(164c)
(ex Jokulfell-93)

MARINE MANAGEMENT SERVICES LTD.

Eaglehurst, Belmont Hill, Douglas, IoM, IM1 4NY (01624 688886/fax 01624 688899)
Managers for:
D.U.K. Shipping Ltd
NORTHERN STAR *(GBR)*   80   1114   719   64,5   10,3   3,5   11   lpg(ch)

MEDWAY SHIPPING LTD.

"Roseville", Danes Hill, Gillingham, Kent, ME7 2TU (01634 851177/fax 01634 581213)

CECIL GILDERS *(GBR)*	57	137	224	27,7	6,5	2,4	7 gen bge
ROINA *(GBR)*	66	172	264	29,4	6,8	2,5	7 gen bge

MERCHANT FERRIES LTD.

North Quay, Heysham Harbour, Morecambe, Lancashire, LA3 2UL (01524 855018/fax 01524 852527)
Proofbrand Ltd
MERCHANT BRAVERY *(BHS)*   78   9368   5290   134,8   21,7   5,0   17   ro(90u)
(ex Jolly Giallo-93, Norwegian Crusader-82, Jolly Giallo-82, Norwegian Crusader-80, launched as Stevi)
MERCHANT
BRILLIANT *(BHS)*   79   9368   5300   133,1   21,7   5,0   17   ro(90u)
(ex Jolly Bruno-93, Norwegian Challenger-82)
MERCHANT VENTURE *(IOM)*   79   6056   3671   119,4   19,5   5,2   17   ro(50u)
(ex Merchant Isle-87, Argentea-87, Med Adriatico-85, Farman-82)
MERCHANT VICTOR *(BHS)*   78   5881   3046   116,3   18,2   5,4   15   ro(50u)
(ex Emadala-90)
Note. Vessels are managed by V SHIPS (UK) *qv*

The **ALPINE GIRL** in the River Mersey and approaching the locks at Eastham   *(Richard Potter)*

MERMAID MARINE MANAGEMENT LTD.

Hoopers Hill House, Angel Lane, Lymington Road, New Milton, Hants, BH25 5PZ (01425 619262/ fax 01425 619237)

Managers for:
Delship Corp

ALPINE GIRL *(BHS)*	75	3984	6418	110,0	16,6	6,9	14	ch tk
(ex Dintel-86, Quimico Lisboa-86, launched as Chemist Lisbon)									

Delship Trading Corp

ALPINE LADY *(BHS)*	77	4009	6433	110,5	16,6	6,9	14	ch tk
(ex Multitank Antares-88, Dommel-87, Quimico Leixoes-86)									

MERSEY SAND SUPPLIERS LTD.

East Side Trafalgar Dock, Liverpool, L3 0AG (0151 236 6646/fax 0151 236 4184)

Operators for:
Norwest Sand & Ballast Co Ltd

NORSTAR *(GBR)*	61	614	1125	47,6	11,0	4,2	9	sd

MEZERON LTD.

East Quay, Ramsey, IoM, IM8 1BG (01624 812302/fax 01624 815613)

GREEBA RIVER *(IOM)*	69	485	713	53,0	8,8	3,3	10	gen
(ex Tora-88, Cynthia June-86, Arklow River-82, Apollo 1-80)									
SILVER RIVER *(IOM)*	68	277	373	44,7	7,4	2,7	10	gen
(ex Nathurn-86, Sea Trent-82, Seacon-71)									

Managers for:
Luscher Marine Ltd

CLAUDIA W *(BLZ)*	61	417	650	54,2	7,6	2,3	8	gen
(ex Eberstein-79)									

MODERN MARINE OPERATIONS LTD.

St Helier, Jersey, Channel Islands

SPEZI *(MLT)*	72	1007	1393	72,7	10,5	3,8	12	gen
(ex Maltese Venture-96, Timrix-95, Ellie-84, Nellie M-82)									

MORLINE LTD.

Morline House, London Road, Barking, Essex, IG11 8BB (0181 507 6000/fax 0181 507 6200)

Managers for:
Beacon 2 Shipping Co Ltd

BEACON 2 *(MLT)*	73	2317	1423	80,5	12,8	4,2	13	ro(115c)
(ex Manilaid-96, Thunar-75)									

Island Navigation Co Ltd

BEACON 3 *(MLT)*	75	7156	6447	129,4	19,2	7,5	17	cc(304c)
(ex Aleksandr Prokofyev-96)									

Runada Shipping Ltd

DANA *(MLT)*	73	1510	2502	80,7	11,3	5,3	11	gen
(ex Lady Dorothy-94, Orchid Star—84, Dolomit-83)									

Nard-Med Shipping Ltd

RUTA *(MLT)*	75	1762	2583	77,8	13,2	5,0	13	gen

(ex Rutland-95, Martindyke-88)

North-Western Shipping Joint Stock Co (A/O "Severo-Zapadnoye Parokhodstvo")

SHEKSNA *(RUS)*	94	2052	2769	82,4	12,5	5,0	12	gen(126c)
INZHENER *(RUS)*	74	8301	6128	124,2	19,6	7,0	16	ro(239c)

(ex Inzhener Machulsky-96)

Bulkway Shipping Ltd

VITA *(MLT)*	69	2723	3950	102,3	14,0	6,2	13	gen

(ex Kaliningrad-96)

NORD SHIP MANAGEMENT LTD.

Office No. 5, Terminal Building, Kirkwall Harbour, Kirkwall, Orkney, KW15 1GD (01856 870124/ fax01856 870125)

CELEBRITY *(GBR)* +	76	633	946	57,6	10,0	3,3	10	gen
COMMODITY *(GBR)* +	75	633	946	57,6	10,0	3,3	10	gen
NORD STAR *(GBR)* +	78	460	727	49,3	9,0	3,2	10	gen

(ex Kava Sound-94, Ordinence-89)

Managers for:

Moonside Compagnie Naviera S.A.

MICHAEL ANE *(HND)*	67	439	655	52,7	8,3	3,0	9	gen

(ex Sanmark-95, Ilen-93, Patmarie-89, Sanmar-87, Union Sun-84, Andre-74)

Note. + *Freight managers* F. T. Everard & Sons Management Ltd *qv*

NORDTANK SHIPPING ApS

Ahlgade 47, 4300 Holbaek, Denmark (+45 59 44 44 66/fax +45 59 44 44 60)

Managers for:

Uni-Tankers m.t."Haahr Bridge"

HAAHR BRIDGE *(IOM)*	67	1131	2104	74,6	10,2	4,9	11	tk

(ex Brevik-95, launched as Venern)

Uni-tankers m.t. "Haahr Trumf"

HAAHR TRUMF *(IOM)*	64	1133	1946	74,4	10,2	4,9	12	tk

(ex Candy I-95, Candy-90, Arholma-85, Smaragd-80, Sibell-79, Cortina-77, Tarnsjo-70)

NORFOLK LINE B.V.

Kranenburgweg 211, Scheveningen, 2583 ER 's Gravenhage, The Netherlands (+31 70 3527402/ fax+31 70 3545579) and

NORFOLK LINE LTD.

Norfolk House, The Dock, Felixstowe, Suffolk, IP11 8UY (01394 603713/fax 01394 603680)

MAERSK FLANDERS *(NLD)*	78	7199	3523	122,9	21,0	4,8	16	ro(90u)

(ex Duke of Flanders-90, Romira-86, Admiral Atlantic-84)

MAERSK EXPORTER *(NLD)*	96	13017	5928	142,4	23,3	5,4	18	ro(120u)
MAERSK IMPORTER *(NLD)*	96	13017	5928	142,4	23,3	5,4	18	ro(120u)

Chartered tonnage:

Oxgate Security Co Ltd

MAERSK ANGLIA *(IOM)*	77	6862	3526	122,9	21,0	4,8	15	ro(90u)

(ex Duke of Anglia-90, Saint Remy-86, Admiral Caribe-82, Admiral Nigeria-79, Admiral Caribe-77)

The companies are part of the A. P. Moller/Maersk Group

NORTH WEST WATER LTD.

Dawson House, Warrington, Cheshire, WA5 3LW (01925 234000)

CONSORTIUM I	*(GBR)*		72	2384	3623	91,0	14,2	5,4	13	sludge
GILBERT J. FOWLER	*(GBR)*	*	71	2384	3623	91,0	14,2	5,4	13	sludge

Note. * *laid up Liverpool*

NORTHERN MARINE MANAGEMENT LTD.

Alba House, 2 Central Avenue, Clydebank Business Park, Clydebank, Dunbartonshire, G81 2QR (0141 9526844/fax 0141 94112791)

Managers for:
Stena Florida Line Ltd

STENA SHIPPER	*(BHS)*	79	12337	9259	168,8	20,2	6,5	17	ro(150u)

(ex Nestor-94, Caribbean Stream-91, Nestor-90, African Gateway-89, Nestor-87, Nestor1-85, Nestor-84)
See also STENA LINE

NORTHWOOD (FAREHAM) LTD.

Riverside House, Upper Wharf, Fareham, Hants, PO16 0NB (01329 235717/fax 01329 822697)

DONALD REDFORD	*(GBR)*		81	681	964	53,5	10,7	3,4	9	sd
MEDINA RIVER	*(GBR)*		69	199	424	41,8	7,7	2,7	9	sand
(ex Colby River-91, Subro Vixen-87, Tower Marie-80)										
NORLEADER	*(GBR)*		67	1592	2420	78,1	13,8	4,7	12	sd
SAND SKUA	*(GBR)*	*	71	1143	1803	67,2	12,5	4,5	10	-

Note: * *Converting back to sand/aggregate suction dredger*

NWS EUROPE LTD.

First Floor, New Hibernia House, Winchester Walk, London, SE1 9AG (0171 403 9779/fax 0171 403 9804)

Chartered tonnage:
OB-Irtysh River Shipping Co

OMSKIY-14	*(RUS)*	78	2426	2500	108,5	15,0	3,0	10	gen(100c)
OMSKIY-102	*(RUS)*	79	2550	2500	108,4	15,0	3,2	10	gen(100c)
OMSKIY-109	*(RUS)*	82	2550	2500	108,4	15,0	3,0	10	gen(100c)

OMINAR SHIPPING CO. LTD.

6 Glenomena Park, Blackrock, Co Dublin, Irish Republic (+ 353 1 2603415/fax +353 1 2601242)

FIONA MAY	*(CYP)*	77	999	1632	61,5	10,4	4,8	9	gen

(ex Serenell-95)

ORCARGO

10A Junction Road, Kirkwall, Orkney, KW15 1LB (01856 873838/fax 01856 876521)

CONTENDER	*(GBR)*	73	2292	1357	79,0	13,3	4,2	15	ro/gen(12u)

(ex Indiana I-92, Indiana-88, Ferruccio-86, Antinea-83)

Trading between Invergordon and Kirkwall, the **CONTENDER** is seen at anchor off the latter port *(Bernard McCall)*

ORKNEY LINE

Hatstone Industrial Estate, Kirkwall, KW15 1ER (01856 873658/fax 01856 873563) and

SHETLAND LINE

Garthspool, Lerwick (01595 2869/fax 01595 2234)

Chartered tonnage:
  Baltic Champ Marine Inc

BALTIC CHAMP *(PAN)*	77	1660	2060	72,0	12,8	4,5	12	gen(132c)
(ex Pico Ruivo-95, Nordlicht II-83)								

PANDORO LTD.

Copse Road, Fleetwood, Lancs, FY7 6HR (01253 777111/fax 01253 771043)

BISON *(GBR)*	75	14387	7078	140,1	19,1	4,7	18	ro(105u)
BUFFALO *(BMU)*	75	10987	4377	141,8	19,6	5,8	18	ro(85u)
IBEX *(BMU)*	79	14077	5024	150,0	23,9	5,1	19	ro(130u)
(ex Norsky-95, Norsea-86, Ibex-80)								
LEOPARD *(GBR)*	77	9085	3775	137,318,1	5,7		18 ro(70u)	
(ex Viking Trader-96, Oyster Bay-83, Manaure VII-83, Caribbean Sky-81, Federal Nova-81, Goya-79, launched as Stena Tender)								
PANTHER *(BMU)*	76	8023	3927	117,9	20,3	5,8	18	ro(60u)
(ex European Clearway-96)								
PUMA *(BMU)*	75	10957	4035	141,8	19,4	5,8	18	ro(85u)
(ex Union Trader-80, Union Melbourne-80)								

Managers for:
  Gateway Investments Ltd

LION *(BHS)*	78	5897	3046	116,3	18,2	5,4	16	ro(55u)
(ex Merchant Valiant-95, Salahala-90)								

Chartered tonnage:
  Seahawk K/S

SEAHAWK *(NIS)*	75	10171	7597	137,6	20,6	7,2	18	ro(80u)
(ex Dana Minerva-96, Fichtelberg-95, Norcliff-93, Fichtelberg-92, Spirit of Dublin-92, Fichtelberg-91, launched as Tor Caledonia)								

P&O EUROPEAN FERRIES LTD.

The Ferry Terminal, Cairnryan, Near Stranraer, Dumfries & Galloway, DG9 8RF (0990 980666/ fax 01581 200282)

EUROPEAN ENDEAVOUR *(GBR)*	78	8097	3767	117,9	20,3	5,1	18	ro(76u)

(ex European Enterprise-88)
Managers for:
Abbey National March Leasing (1) Ltd

EUROPEAN TRADER *(GBR)*	75	8007	3953	117,9	20,3	5,8	18	ro(76u)

P&O EUROPEAN FERRIES (DOVER) LTD.

Channel House, Channel View Road, Dover, Kent, CT17 9TJ (01304 86300/fax 01304863223)

Managers for:
Hamton Ltd

EUROPEAN HIGHWAY *(GBR)*	92	22986	7550	179,7	28,3	6,3	21	ro(124u)

Sutten Ltd

EUROPEAN PATHWAY *(GBR)*	91	22986	7550	179,7	28,3	6,3	21	ro(124u)
EUROPEAN SEAWAY *(GBR)*	91	22986	6584	179,7	28,3	6,3	21	ro(124u)

P&O NORTH SEA FERRIES LTD.

King George Dock, Hedon Road, Hull, HU9 5QA (01482 795141/fax 01482 712170) and Ferry Centre, The Dock, Felixstowe, Suffolk, IP11 8TB (01394 604100/fax 01394 604203)

EUROPEAN FREEWAY *(GBR)*	78	21162	6594	184,6	25,3	6,4	17	ro(140u)

(ex Cerdic Ferry-91, Stena Transporter-86, Syria-83, Alpha Enterprise-79)

EUROPEAN TIDEWAY *(GBR)*	77	21162	8672	184,6	25,3	6,4	17	ro(140u)

(ex Doric Ferry-91, Hellas-86, Alpha Progress-79, Stena Runner-77)
Managed and chartered tonnage:
Partenreederei m.s. "Gabriele Wehr"

GABRIELE WEHR *(DEU)*	78	7635	4322	141,3	17,4	5,2	17	ro(70u)

(ex Sari-93, Gabriele Wehr-92, Tor Anglia-85, Gabriele Wehr-82)
Norbank C.V.

NORBANK *(NLD)*	93	17464	6791	166,8	23,9	6,0	23	ro(156u)

Equipment Leasing (Properties) Ltd

NORBAY *(GBR)*	94	17464	6722	166,8	23,9	6,0	23	ro(156u)

Norcape Shipping B.V.

NORCAPE *(NLD)*	79	14087	5024	150,0	20,7	5,1	19	ro(121u)

(ex Tipperary-89, launched as Puma)
B&N Rederi AB

NORCOVE *(SWE)*	77	10279	6671	142,2	19,3	7,0	18	ro(105u)

(ex Cupria-95, Canopus-92, Finnforest-82, Rolita-79)
Oy Rettig Ab

NORKING *(FIN)*	80	17884	7984	170,9	23,0	7,6	19	ro(150u)

(ex Bore King-91)

NORQUEEN *(FIN)*	80	17884	7984	170,9	23,0	7,6	19	ro(150u)

(ex Bore Queen-91)
NatWest Specialist Finance Ltd

PRIDE OF FLANDERS *(GBR)*	78	16776	5455	151,0	23,6	6,5	17	ro(110u)

(ex Nordic Ferry-92, Merzario Hispania-79, Merzario Espania-78)
BMBF (No 15) Ltd

PRIDE OF SUFFOLK *(GBR)*	78	16776	5455	151,0	21,7	6,5	17	ro(110u)

(ex Baltic Ferry-92, Stena Transporter-80, Finnrose-80, Stena Transporter-79)
Partenreederei m.s. "Thomas Wehr"

THOMAS WEHR *(DEU)*	77	7628	4322	141,3	17,4	5,2	17	ro(75u)

(ex Hornlink-94, Fuldatal-94, Santa Maria-93, Mana-93, Thomas Wehr-93, Dana Germania-86, Tor Neerlandia-85 , Thomas Wehr-82, Wacro Express-78, launched as Thomas Wehr)

The NORKING hurries through Tees Bay　　　　　　　　　　　　　　　　　　*(Richard Potter)*

P&O FERRYMASTERS LTD.

Station House, Stamford New Road, Altrincham, Cheshire, WA14 1ER (0161 928-6333/fax 0161 926-9592)
Managers for:
　West Merchant Bank Ltd, BNP Leasing Ltd, C.T.S.B. Leasing Ltd & A.E.B.(UK)Ltd

ELK *(GBR)*	77	14374	9700	163,6	21,7	7,3	18	ro(135u)

Chartered tonnage:
　Tidero A/S

TIDERO STAR *(NIS)*	78	9698	5500	152,3	19,5	6,2	17	ro(90u)

(ex Anzere-91)

P&O SCOTTISH FERRIES LTD.

Jamieson's Quay, PO Box 5, Aberdeen, AB9 8DL (01224 589111/fax 01224 584378)

ST ROGNVALD *(GBR)*	70	5297	3801	103,8	18,8	5,0	16	ro(43u)

(ex Marino Torre-90, Rhone-87, Rhonetal-75, Norcape-74, launched as Rhonetal)
Agents for:
　Strandfaraskip Landsins
Chartered tonnage:
　Clare Business Ltd

CLARE *(NIS)*	72	5617	2850	114,9	17,4	5,3	17	ro(65u)

(ex Dana Baltica-96, Vinzia E.-94, Norcrest-93, Wesertal-92, Meyer Express-73, Wesertal-72)

PETROLEUM SHIPPING LTD.

4th Floor, Mountbatten House, Grovesnor Square, Southampton, SO15 2UX (01703 821200/
fax 01703 821390)
Managers for:
　Esso Marine UK Ltd

PETRO AVON *(GBR)*	81	2386	3122	91,3	13,1	5,6	12	oil/bit tk
(ex Esso Avon-94)								
PETRO MERSEY *(GBR)*	72	11898	20510	166,5	22,8	9,2	15	tk
(ex Esso Mersey-94)								
PETRO SEVERN *(GBR)*	75	11897	20087	166,5	22,9	9,2	15	tk
(ex Esso Severn-94)								
PETRO TYNE *(GBR)*	74	13340	22333	161,2	23,6	9,8	13	tk

(ex Esso Tyne-94, Esso Saint Petersburg-90, Esso Callunda-85)

PIKE WARD LTD.

Old Quay, Teignmouth, Devon, TQ14 8EU (01626 772311/fax 01626 770218)
Managers for:
Bartlett Bros (Hauliers) Ltd

TARWAY *(GBR)*	58	80	140	25,6	5,2	2,1	7	sd

Note: Also employed on maintenance dredging at Teignmouth

PORT OF PEMBROKE LTD.

Sunderland House, The Old Royal Dockyard, Pembroke Dock, Dyfed, SA72 6TD (01646 683981/
fax 01646 687394)

G . D. DISTRIBUTOR *(GBR)*	74	589	693	59,1	10,0	2,5	10	bk tk bge

(ex Shell Distributor-91, Harty-79)

PRATT ALAN J., ANNETTE, DAVID A., & MICHAEL

770 Lower Rainham Road, Rainham, Gillingham, Kent, ME8 7UB (01634 234147/fax 01634 234147)
Managers for:
Bartlett Creek Shipping Ltd

LOCATOR *(GBR)*	70	181	315	31,7	6,8	2,6	7	gen
LODELLA *(GBR)*	70	181	315	31,7	6,8	2,6	7	gen
ROAN *(GBR)*	61	138	250	27,7	6,5	2,5	7	gen bge
ROGUL *(GBR)*	65	172	254	29,4	6,8	2,6	7	gen

J. J. PRIOR (TRANSPORT) LTD.

Ballast Quay, Fingringhoe, Essex, CO5 7DB (01206 729 412/fax 01206 729 551)

BERT PRIOR *(GBR)*	61	175	289	32,9	6,8	2,5	7	sand
BRENDA PRIOR *(GBR)*	68	198	279	32,3	7,0	2,7	7	sand
(ex Cheryl M-87, Kiption-84)								
JAMES PRIOR *(GBR)*	63	191	300	34,1	6,8	2,6	7	sand
(ex James P-95)								
MARK PRIOR *(GBR)*	69	191	295	31,7	6,8	2,6	7	sand
(ex Lobe-94)								
PETER P *(GBR)*	15	186	279	33,5	6,5	2,4	7	sand
(ex Fence-64, X57)								

Chartered Tonnage:
Alan Jenner

ROFFEN *(GBR)*	65	172	261	29,4	7,1	2,5	7	sand

NAVIERA QUIMICA S.A.

Apartment 105, Edificio Netro, Calle Ibaigane 15-2°, 48930 Las Arenas, Viscaya, Spain (+34 94 464 10 99/
fax +34 94 464 29 58)
Managers for:
Tanis Ltd

BENCENO *(IOM)*	77	2612	3971	101,0	14,3	6,4	15	ch tk

Titus Shipping Ltd

ESTIRENO *(IOM)*	77	2612	3970	101,0	14,3	6,4	15	ch tk

RADMOOR SHIPPING LTD.

27 Waterloo Road, Wolverhampton, West Midlands, WV1 4DJ

HOLM SOUND *(GBR)*	69	392	609	44,4	7,9	3,2	9	gen
(ex Gore-87, Eloquence-85)								

THE RAMSEY STEAMSHIP CO. LTD.

13 North Quay, Douglas, IoM, IM1 4LE (01624 673557/fax 01624 620460)

BEN ELLAN *(IOM)*	81	538	824	50,0	9,3	3,4	9	gen
(ex River Tamar-90)								
BEN MAYE *(IOM)*	79	548	805	48,8	9,1	3,6	10	gen
(ex Vendome-95, Peroto-94)								
BEN VANE *(IOM)*	77	541	772	50,2	9,0	3,4	9	gen
(ex Bulk Moon-88, Julia S-81)								

RMS (EUROPE) LTD

Boothferry Terminal, Bridge Street, Goole, DN14 5SS (01405 720707/fax 01405 720740)

Chartered tonnage:

BOLDER *(NLD)*								
(ex Eben Haezer-96)	86	1272	1500	81,2	10,4	3,5	10	gen(81c)
Paul Hase m.s. "Pandor" KG								
PANDOR *(DEU)*	80	1441	1795	81,0	11,3	3,3	10	gen

The Douglas - registered WESERSTERN outward bound in the River Elbe   *(Dominic McCall)*

RIGEL SCHIFFAHRTS GmbH

World Trade Center, Birkenstrasse 15, 28195 Bremen, Germany (+49 0421 1691450/fax +49 0421 1691455)

Managers for:

Chemshipping Ltd

ODERSTERN *(IOM)*	92	5480	9028	109,7	17,7	8,5	12	oil/ch tk
Chem Carriers Ltd								
WESERSTERN *(IOM)*	92	5480	9028	109,7	17,7	8,5	12	oil/ch tk

RHEINTAINER LINIE

19 Deichstrasse, Hamburg, Germany (+49 4036 120300)

Chartered tonnage:
Harren & Partner Schiffahrts GmbH & Co KG m.s. "Rhein Lagan"

RHEIN MASTER *(ATG)*	94	3790	4766	100,6	16,5	5,9	15	gen(380c)

(ex Rhein Lagan-96, Paranga-95)
m.s. "Sybille" Reederei Ludtke KG

RHEIN MERCHANT *(DEU)*	91	3125	4485	89,1	16,2	6,1	14	gen(260c)

(ex Sybille-95, Baltic Bridge-93, Sybille-93)
Schiffartsgesellschaft m.s. "Deneb" Heinz Moje KG

RHEIN PARTNER *(DEU)*	94	3992	5350	101,1	18,4	6,6	15	gen(509c)

(ex Rhein Liffey-95, completed as Deneb)

J. R. RIX & SONS LTD.

Witham House, 45 Spyvee Street, Hull, HU8 7JR (01482 224422 /fax 01482 210719)

Managers for:
Jemrix Shipping Co Ltd
BREYDON

VENTURE *(GBR)*	77	562	1036	45,9	10,0	3,9	9	gen

(ex Wis-86)
Jonrix Shipping Co Ltd

JONRIX *(BHS)*	77	999	2097	79,0	12,5	4,8	11	gen(104c)

(ex Langeland II-94, Langeland-83)
Lizrix Shipping Co Ltd

LIZRIX *(BHS)*	77	2019	3050	82,3	13,9	5,3	12	gen

(ex Yorksee-96, Katharina-90, Karlsvik-86, launched as Eriesee)
The Magrix Shipping Co Ltd

MAGRIX *(GBR)*	76	1220	1897	78,4	10,8	4,1	11	gen

(ex The Dutch-87, Tanja Holwerda-87, Roelof Holwerda-81)
T. & S. Rix Ltd

RIX EAGLE *(GBR)*	90	292	500	50,0	6,0	3,0	8	tk bge
RIX FALCON *(GBR)*	60	172	250	43,3	5,4	2,1	8	tk bge

(ex Burtondale H-92)

RIX HARRIER *(GBR)*	79	572	1046	45,7	9,5	3,9	9	tk

(ex Breydon Enterprise-96, Wib-87)

RIX KESTREL *(GBR)*	57	206	320	50,9	5,4	2,3	8	tk bge

(ex Burdale H-93)

RIX MERLIN *(GBR)*	64	299	520	55,0	6,6	2,5	10	tk bge

(ex Artemisium-96)

RIX OSPREY *(GBR)*	59	207	300	50,9	5,2	2,3	8	tk bge

(ex Beldale H-96)

ROLF ROHWEDDER REEDEREI

Sonsbecker Strasse 40-44, 46509 Xanten, Germany (+49 02801 71430/fax +49 02801 714315)

Managers for:
Silvaplana Shipping Co (C.I.) Ltd

MEDWAY *(BHS)*	77	1475	2271	69,0	13,5	4,5	9	gen

(ex Sea Medway-94)

SAL AGENCY LTD.

Container Terminal, South Bank Quay, Dublin 4, Irish Republic (+ 353 1 6672727/fax + 353 1 6672737)
Agents only for:
Kapitan Manfred Draxl Schiffahrts GmbH & Co KG m.v. "Dorte"

MATHILDA *(ATG)*	94	3958	5350	108,0	16,0	6,0	16	cc(448c)
(ex Dorte-94)								

SANDFORD SHIP MANAGEMENT LTD.

Neptune House, Sandford, Ventnor, IoW, PO38 3AN (01983 840133/fax 01983 840190)
Managers for:
Marine Atlantic Inc

MARINE EVANGELINE *(BHS)*	74	2793	1856	110,1	17,5	5,8	18	ro(45u)
(ex Spirit of Boulogne-95, Marine Evangeline-93, Duke of Yorkshire-78)								

SCOTTISH AGGREGATES LTD.

6 Union Street, Bridge of Allan, Stirlingshire (01786 834055/fax 01786 834381)

TAYSAND *(GBR)*	58	150	280	30,8	6,3	3,0	7	sd
(ex Clyde Enterprise-96)								

SEACON LTD.

The London Steel Terminal, Express Wharf, 38 West Ferry Road, London, E14 8LW (0171 987-1291/
fax 0171 987-2915)
Chartered tonnage:
Briese Schiffahrts GmbH & Co KG m.s. "Dukegat"

SEA DOURO *(ATG)*	88	910	1085	69,1	9,5	3,0	10	gen(36c)
(Launched as Leda)								

m.s. "Elbe" Kapitan Bernd Wittkowski KG

SEA ELBE *(ATG)*	86	1636	1910	82,5	11,3	3,8	10	gen(44c)
(ex Silke-95)								

C.V. Scheepvaartonderneming "Futura"

SEA MAAS *(NLD)*	95	1682	2500	81,7	11,0	4,5	11	gen
(ex Futura-96)								

Reederei Frank Dahl m.s. "Merlan"

SEA MERLAN *(ATG)*	78	1495	1548	76,8	11,5	3,4	11	gen(62c)
(Launched as Merlan)								

Reederei Frank Dahl m.s. "Orade" KG

SEA ORADE *(DEU)*	90	1354	1699	77,0	11,4	3,2	10	gen(94c)
(Launched as Orade)								

Natissa Shipping Ltd

SEA RHONE *(VCT)*	95	1554	2044	81,6	11,4	3,7	10	gen

Rhone Shipping Ltd

SEA RUHR *(VCT)*	95	1554	2044	81,6	11,4	3,7	10	gen

m.s. "Neckar" Kapitan Bernd Wittkowski KG

SEA THAMES *(ATG)*	85	1616	1922	82,5	11,4	3,8	10	gen(67c)
(ex Kurt Jensen-94)								

See also DUNDALK SHIPOWNERS & TORBULK

The SEA RHONE heads into the River Humber   *(Ray Johnson)*

SEASCOT SHIPMANAGEMENT LTD.

45 Carrick Street, Glasgow, G2 8PJ (0141 226-3733/fax 0141 204-3276)
Managers for:
North Bay Shipping Ltd
LESZEK G *(POL)*   77   1991   3285   91,5   13,3   5,1   12   gen(60c)
(ex Leslie Gault-92)

SEATRUCK FERRIES LTD.

North Quay, Heysham Harbour, Morecambe, Lancashire LA3 2UL (01524 853512/fax 01524 853549)
Chartered tonnage:
Octogon Shipping & Service
BOLERO *(ROM)*   85   9983   6704   140,1   23,5   6,5   14   ro(90u)
(ex Tuzla-96, launched as Spiegelberg)
Starship Co Ltd
RIVERDANCE *(BHS)*   77   6041   3046   116,3   18,2   5,4   15   ro(50u)
(ex Sally Eurobridge-96, Eurobridge-94, Sally Eurobridge-94, Schiaffino-93, Tikal-89, Halla-88, Mashala-86)

SEAWARD ENGINEERING

974 Pollokshaws Road, Glasgow, G41 2HA (0141 632 4910 /fax 0141 636 1194)
SULBY RIVER *(IOM)*   71   196   269   30,6   7,1   2,4   8   gen
(ex Subro Venture-84)
Note. Laid up repairing at Bowling

SEAWHEEL LTD.

Western House, Hadleigh Road, Ipswich, Suffolk, IP2 0HB (01473 222000/fax 01473 230083)
Chartered tonnage:
CV Scheepvaartonderneming "Heereplein"

HEEREPLEIN *(NLD)*	96	2035	2800	90,0	13,8	4,2	13 gen(205c)

Grade Universe Shipping Co Ltd

JORUND *(CYP)*	76	2240	2560	81,4	13,4	5,0	14 gen(150c)

(ex Seefalke-85)
m.s. "Linda Buck" Schiffahrts KG

LINDA BUCK *(ATG)*	85	2295	2584	95,9	14,2	4,1	10 ro(180c)

(ex Britannia-96, RMS Britannia-93, Linda Buck-93)
m.s. "Rolf Buck" Schiffahrts KG

ROLF BUCK *(ATG)*	85	2295	2591	95,9	14,2	4,1	10 ro(180c)

The ROLF BUCK passes Reedness on her way up the River Ouse to Goole with a cargo of containers *(David H. Smith)*

SEVERN SANDS LTD.

14 Westgate Chambers, Commercial Street, Newport, Gwent (01633 220842/fax 01633 253976)

SEVERN SANDS *(GBR)*	60	515	676	51,7	9,2	3,7	9 sd

(ex Ferlas-95, Le Ferlas-89, Isca-77)
Managers for:
Crossavon Ltd

RHONE *(GBR)*	66	276	448	46,4	7,6	2,6	9 sd

SHELL U.K. OIL LTD.

Room 789, Shell-Mex House, Strand, PO Box 148, London, WC2R 0DX (0171 257-3000/fax 0171 257-3440)
Managers for:
Shell U.K. Ltd

ACHATINA *(GBR)*	68	1580	2654	84,3	12,5	4,7	14	tk
(ex Shell Craftsman-93, Ardrossan-79)								
AMORIA *(GBR)*	81	1926	3027	79,3	13,2	5,5	12	tk
(ex Shell Marketer-93)								
ARIANTA *(GBR)*	82	1926	3027	79,3	13,2	5,5	12	tk
(ex Shell Technician-93)								
ASPRELLA *(GBR)*	81	1926	3027	79,2	13,2	5,5	12	tk
(ex Shell Seafarer-93)								
Time Chartered tonnage:								
Shell Tankers B.V.								
ACILA *(NLD)*	82	8806	11548	140,8	21,2	7,3	14	tk
(ex Shelltrans-94)								

Shell's ASPRELLA sails up the Manchester Ship Canal to load a cargo of refined products from the company's Stanlow refinery *(Dominic McCall)*

SLOMAN NEPTUN SCHIFFAHRTS - AKTIENGESELLSCHAFT

Langenstrasse 52-54, Postfach 101469, 28195 Bremen, Germany (+49 0421 1763314/fax +49 0421 1763313)
Managers for:
Deltagas Shipping Co Ltd

DELTAGAS *(LBR)*	92	3011	3700	88,4	14,2	6,2	14	lpg
Gammagas Shipping Co Ltd								
GAMMAGAS *(LBR)*	92	3703	4447	99,4	15,0	6,5	15	lpg

SOENDERBORG REDERIAKTIESELSKAB (SONDERBORG STEAMSHIP CO. LTD.)

Havnevej 18, PO Box 20, 6320 Egernsund, Denmark (+45 74 441435/fax +45 74 441475)
Managers for:
Clovis Navigation S.A.
GERARD PATRICK

PURCELL *(PAN)*	70	2978	2568	88,5	13,9	5,5	13	l/v

(ex Deichtor-83, Lubbecke-83, Ibesca Belgica-80, Ibesca Britannia-78, Lubbecke-77)
K/S Philomena

PHILOMENA PURCELL *(DIS)*	73	3013	2650	88,3	13,0	5,0	13	l/v

(ex Esteflut-82)

SOUTH COAST SHIPPING CO. LTD.

Canute Chambers, 88 Canute Road, Southampton, SO1 4 3AB (01703 333212/fax 01703 334528)

SAND HARRIER *(GBR)*	90	3751	5916	99,0	16,5	6,6	11	sd
SAND HERON *(GBR)*	90	3751	5916	99,0	16,5	6,4	11	sd
SAND SWAN *(GBR)*	70	1204	1944	66,6	12,5	4,4	10	sd
SAND SWIFT *(GBR)*	69	1204	1944	66,5	12,5	4,3	10	sd
SAND WADER *(GBR)*	71	3082	5209	96,5	17,0	6,2	11	sd
New building (Merwede) May	98		9000					sd

Managers for:
East Coast Aggregates Ltd

SAND KESTREL *(GBR)*	74	3110	4722	98,7	18,2	5,1	13	sd

(ex Bowherald-94)

SAND KITE *(GBR)*	74	3110	4425	98,7	18,2	5,1	13	sd

(ex Bowknight-93)
Baring Brothers & Container Leasing Co Ltd

SAND SERIN *(GBR)*	74	1283	2120	66,6	12,2	4,8	10	sd
SAND WEAVER *(GBR)*	75	3497	5271	96,4	16,7	6,1	12	sd

SOUTH WEST WATER PLC

Exewater, Eagle Way, Exeter, Devon, EX2 7HY (01392 445544/fax 01392 444694)

COUNTESS WEAR *(GBR)*	63	237	366	37,5	7,5	3,1	8	sludge

(ex S.W.2-75)

ST HELIER PORT SERVICES LTD.

New North Quay, St Helier, Jersey, Channel Islands, (01534 870300/fax 01534 830234)
Managers for:
Camas UK Ltd

RONEZ *(GBR)*	82	870	1117	64,7	10,1	3,5	10	cem

STENA LINE LTD.

3rd Floor, East Wing, Charter House, Park Street, Ashford, Kent, TN24 8EX (01233 647022/ fax 01233 202321)

Managers for:
Stena Equipment & Aircraft Leasing Ltd

STENA CALEDONIA *(GBR)*	81	12619	2206	129,7	21,6	4,8	19	ro/px(62u)*
(ex St David-91)								
STENA CHALLENGER *(GBR)*	91	18523	4650	157,3	24,3	5,5	17	ro/px(120u)*

NWS 11 Ltd

STENA GALLOWAY *(GBR)*	80	12175	1895	129,4	21,6	4,7	18	ro/px(62u)*
(ex Galloway Princess-91)								

Lily Shipping B.V.

STENA SEATRADER *(NLD)*	73	17991	6850	182,7	22,1	6,2	17	ro(130u)
(ex Svea Link-90, Svealand av Malmo-87, Svealand-82)								

Chartered tonnage:
Poseidon Schiffahrt AG

ROSEBAY *(CYP)*	76	13700	5233	135,5	21.8	6,1	17	ro(100u)
(ex Rosebay-96, Transgermania-93)								

Note: * *trading freight only   See also* NORTHERN MARINE MANAGEMENT
Chartered tonnage operated by Stena Freight, Harwich
Heinz Ehler KG

ANKE EHLER *(DEU)*	90	2642	3100	90,0	13,0	4,6	12	gen(198c)

Uwe von Allworden KG m.s. "Hera"

HERA *(DEU)*	90	2606	3240	90,0	13,0	4,6	11	gen(198c)

AB STENA MARINE

Danmarksterminalen, Masthuggetskajen, 40519 Gothenburg, Sweden (+46 031 858000/fax +46 031 120651)

Managers for:
Stena Carrier Ltd

STENA CARRIER *(CYM)*	78	13117	8661	151,0	20,5	7,3	16	ro(562c)
(ex Jolly Smeraldo-83, Jolly Bruno-82, Stena Carrier-82, Imparca Miami-81, Stena Carrier-80, Imparca Express I-80)								

The **HARTING** prepares to leave the Birkenhead dock system   *(Bernard McCall)*

STEPHENSON CLARKE SHIPPING LTD.

Eldon Court, Percy Street, Newcastle upon Tyne, NE99 1TD (0191 232-2184/fax 0191 261-1156)

AMETHYST *(GBR)*	87	8254	11901	142,9	20,1	7,2	12	bulk
(ex Cardona-93)								
BIRLING *(IOM)*	77	2795	4300	91,3	14,6	5,4	14	gen
DALLINGTON *(GBR)*	75	7788	12140	137,6	18,7	7,9	14	gen
DONNINGTON *(GBR)*	75	7788	12134	137,6	18,7	7,9	14	gen
DURRINGTON *(IOM)*	81	7788	11990	137,6	18,7	7,9	14	gen
EMERALD *(IOM)*	78	2795	4300	91,3	14,6	5,5	14	gen
HARTING *(IOM)*	81	2813	4300	91,3	14,6	5,8	12	gen(32c)
STEYNING *(IOM)*	83	2808	4300	91,3	14,6	5,8	12	gen(32c)
STORRINGTON *(IOM)*	82	7788	11990	137,6	18,7	7,9	14	gen
Managers for:								
Joint Lease Ltd								
JEVINGTON *(GBR)*	77	7702	12328	127,4	19,5	8,1	13	bulk
(ex Elizabete-89, Garrison Point-88)								
Mobil Shipping Co Ltd								
LUBCHEM *(GBR)*	73	1999	3310	93,3	14,0	5,4	12	ch tk
(ex Mobil Lubchem-91)								
Container Finance Ltd								
NORTHUMBRIAN								
WATER *(GBR)*	77	1068	1654	72,5	14,6	3,4	12	sludge
Time chartered tonnage:								
Aldrington KS								
ALDRINGTON *(BHS)*	78	4297	6570	103,6	16,1	7,0	14	gen
Ashington KS								
ASHINGTON *(BHS)*	79	4297	6570	103,6	16,1	7,0	14	gen
Stephenson Clarke Shipping Ltd demise chartered to Point Shipping Co, Dundalk								
DUNANY *(IRL)*	83	1785	2535	77,1	13,2	5,0	12	gen
(ex Cowdray-94, Ballygrainey-90)								
HOPE *(IRL)*	82	1785	2535	77,1	13,2	5,0	12	gen
(ex Shoreham-93, Ballygarvey-90)								
Arendal Bulk Ship K/S								
GEM *(NIS)*	74	7482	11848	135,7	19,3	8,3	12	bulk
(ex Guardo-92)								
James Fisher & Sons (Liverpool) Ltd								
LANCING *(GBR)*	76	1943	3109	83,5	14,1	5,2	12	gen
(ex Ballykern-90, Baxtergate-80)								
WORTHING *(GBR)*	75	1938	3000	83,5	14,1	5,1	12	gen
(ex Ballykelly-90, Lis Danielsen-79)								
Stephenson Clarke Shipping Ltd demise chartered to Losinjska Plovibda Brodarstvo, Mali Losinj								
WASHINGTON *(HRV)*	77	6400	9008	127,0	18,7	7,6	14	gen

STOLT-NIELSEN SHIPPING LTD.

Aldwych House, 71-91 Aldwych, London, WC2B 4HN (0171 404 4455/fax 0171 831 3100)

Commercial operators for;

Stolt Avocet Inc								
STOLT AVOCET *(NIS)*	92	3853	5749	99,9	16,8	6,8	12	ch tk
Stolt Shipholding (Gibraltar) Ltd								
STOLT DIPPER *(NIS)*	92	3206	4794	96,3	15,1	6,2	13	ch tk
(ex Margit Terkol-96, Stolt Margit Terkol-94)								
STOLT GUILLEMOT *(NIS)*	93	3204	4698	96,4	15,3	6,2	13	ch tk
(ex Sasi Terkol-96)								

STOLT KITE *(NIS)*	92	3206	4794	96,4	15,3	6,2	13	ch tk
(ex Randi Terkol-96)								
STOLT KITTIWAKE *(NIS)*	93	3204	4710	96,4	15,3	6,2	13	ch tk
(ex Astrid Terkol-96)								
STOLT PETREL *(NIS)*	92	3206	4761	96,4	15,3	6,2	13	ch tk
(ex Edny Terkol-96)								
STOLT TERN *(NIS)*	91	3206	4759	96,4	15,3	6,2	13	ch tk
(ex Jytte Terkol-96, Stolt Jytte Terkol-92								
Stolt Kestrel Inc								
STOLT KESTREL *(NIS)*	92	3853	5741	99,9	17,1	6,8	12	ch tk
Fleet National Bank								
STOLT KINGFISHER *(NIS)*	86	1970	3283	88,0	13,6	5,5	12	ch tk
(ex Kingfisher-95, Stolt Kingfisher-94, Trusty-88)								
New buildings (6) (Inma, Italy)								
from Dec 97			5200					ch tk

STONEBANK SHIPPING

Liversedge, W. Yorkshire

JOHNO *(GBR)*	61	249	414	42,0	7,6	2,4	8	gen
(ex Ahmed Issa-92, Bandick-90, Christine-74)								

SWINSHIP MANAGEMENT B.V.

Ringdijk 516, 2987 VZ Ridderkerk, Netherlands (+31 0180 419002 /fax +31 0180 411341)

Bareboat charter:
  Onesimus Dorey (Shipowners) Ltd

TEAL I *(VCT)*	74	891	1400	60,9	9,8	4,3	11	gen
(ex Hoxa Sound-94, Murell-88)								

TORBULK LTD.

The Old Rectory, Bargate, Grimsby, Nth Lincolnshire, DN34 4SY (01472 242363/fax 01472 242329)

Fosseway Shipping Ltd								
FOSSELAND *(BHS)*	79	1059	1559	66,9	10,8	4,1	11	gen(58c)
(ex Perelle-94)								
Managers for:								
Oakland Shipping Ltd								
OAKLAND *(BHS)*	78	1059	1559	66,9	10,8	4,1	11	gen(58c)
(ex Belgrave-95)								
Estuary Shipping Ltd								
SEA HUMBER *(BHS)* *	77	1602	2139	69,0	13,5	4,5	10	gen
Swanland Shipping Ltd								
SWANLAND *(BRB)*	77	1978	3150	81,0	13,9	5,4	12	gen
(ex Elsborg-96, Artemis-94, Elsborg-88, Carebeka IX-83)								
Bareboat charter:								
Little Whiting & Tedford Ltd								
SEA TRENT *(BRB)* *	77	1475	2273	69,0	13,5	4,5	9	gen
(ex Sea Avon-96)								

Note. * *Time chartered to* SEACON LTD *qv See also* Onesimus Dorey (Shipowners) Ltd *under* F. T. EVERARD

Torbulk's FOSSELAND is seen in the Bristol Channel off Newport *(Danny Lynch)*

TRANSMARINE MANAGEMENT ApS

1st Floor, Holbergsgade 26, 1057 Copenhagen, Denmark (+45 33 93 25 25/fax +45 33 93 89 81)
Managers for:
Prime Commercial Investment Ltd

AMARANT *(IOM)*	69	1726	2545	86,4	12,0	5,2	12	ch tk
(ex Kimia Maju-86, Chemical Sprinter-84)								
AMETIST *(IOM)*	93	2728	4572	94,5	15,0	6,1	15	ch tk
(ex Hang Chang No.8-96)								

TYNE WATER BOATS LTD.

9 King George Road, South Shields, Tyne & Wear, NE34 0SP (0191 427 0991 & 0860 899928/
fax 0191 425 2340)

ABERCRAIG *(GBR)*	45	138	180	31,7	6,0	2,2	8	wt tk bge
(ex Ernie Spearing-74, Attunity-67, VWL 12-52, MOB 9-46)								
HARCUSS *(GBR)*	32	96	150	26,5	5,2	2,7	8	wt tk bge

UB SHIPPING LTD.

Renaissance House, 131 Shoreditch High Street, London E1 6JE (0171 613-5420/fax 0171 613-7201)
Managers for:
Ugland Container Carriers Ltd

TEUTONIA *(CYM)*	72	2441	2685	92,1	13,1	4,7	13	gen(180c)
(ex Ocean Pride-88, Teutonia-87)								
UB PANTHER *(CYM)*	77	3622	4450	97,5	16,1	5,7	14	gen(343c)
(ex Geranta-94, Gracechurch Star-91, Geranta-89, Karen Oltman-89, Neerlandia-85, Karen Oltman-78)								

Managers through AS Gerrards Rederi for:
K/S Gerina

GERINA *(NIS)*	73	2130	2460	81,4	13,4	4,9	14	gen(165c)
(ex Rendsburg-90, Anna Becker-84, Killarney-79, Anna Becker-77, Scol Enterprise-77, lchd as Anna Becker)								

K/S Gerlena
GERLENA *(NIS)*   74   2130   2503   81,4   13,4   4,9   13 gen(165c)
(ex Achat-89, Osteland-82, Nic Trader-79, Osteland-79, Thunar-76, Osteland-74)
K/S Gerland
Chartered tonnage operated by UB Shipping Liner Services:
  m.s. "Berolin" Ernst-August von Allworden und Dirk Jager KG
UB JAGUAR *(ATG)*   94   3992   5350   100,0   18,4   6,6   15 gen(509c)
(ex Iberian Bridge-96, Berolin-94)
  Waterblue Maritime Ltd
UB LAPTALI M *(MLT)*   77   2581   3618   93,3   13,5   6,1   12 gen(121c)
(ex Alpha Marine-95, Cotinsa Catalunya-94, Alraigo-91)
  m.s. "Holger" Holger und Herbert Szidat KG
UB LION *(ATG)*   95   3999   5207   100,0   18,5   6,6   15 gen(508c)
(ex Holger-95)
  Reederei m.s. "Caravelle" KG Gebr.Winter Schiffahrtsgesellschaft mbH und Co
UB PUMA *(DEU)*   96   12029   14643   157,1   23,5   9,3   18 cc(1122c)
(Completed as Caravelle)
  m.s. "Jacob Becker" Bernd Becker K.G.
UB TIGER *(ATG)*   95   3999   5315   100,0   18,5   6,6   15 gen(508c)
(ex Jacob Becker-95)
Note. Also owners/managers of tonnage operating worldwide

UNION TRANSPORT GROUP PLC

Imperial House, 21-25 North Street, Bromley, Kent, BR1 1SJ (0181 290-1234/fax 0181 289-1592)
UNION ARBO   *(BHS)*   84   1522   1899   82,5   11,4   3,5   10 gen(80c)
(ex Birka-94)
UNION JUPITER   *(BRB)*   90   2230   3274   99,7   12,6   4,3   11 gen(114c)
UNION MARS   *(BRB)*   81   935   1457   69,9   11,3   3,4   11 gen
UNION MERCURY   *(BRB)*   91   2252   3106   81,5   14,4   5,3   12 gen
(ex Donon-93)
UNION MOON   *(BRB)*   85   1543   2362   87,7   11,1   3,9   10 gen(98c)

The **UNION MOON** owned by Union Transport, is a regular caller at Teignmouth. Here she is arriving from Garston to load a cargo of clay
(Bob Collins)

UNION NEPTUNE *(BRB)*	85	1543	2376	87,7	11,1	3,9	10	gen(98c)
UNION PEARL *(BRB)*	90	2230	3274	99,7	13,0	4,3	11	gen(114c)
(ex Bromley Pearl-95)								
UNION PLUTO *(BRB)*	84	1522	1899	82,5	11,4	3,5	10	gen(80c)
(ex Phonix 1-95, Phoenix-94, Osterburg-87)								
UNION SUN *(BRB)*	85	1543	2376	87,7	11,1	3,9	10	gen(98c)
UNION TITAN *(BRB)*	86	1543	2376	87,7	11,1	3,9	10	gen(98c)
UNION TOPAZ *(BRB)*	85	1543	2362	87,7	11,1	3,9	10	gen(98c)
(ex Bromley Topaz-92, Union Topaz-90)								
UNION VENUS *(BRB)*	84	1522	1899	82,5	11,4	3,5	10	gen(48c)
(ex Pinguin-95, Hansa-89)								

Managers for:
Rederij H. Steenstra

ANNE S *(NLD)*	86	1139	1601	79,1	10,4	3,3	11	gen(80c)
DOUWE S *(NLD)*	87	1311	1771	79,7	11,3	3,7	10	gen(78c)
(ex Torpe-94)								

Rederij P. Doorenweerd

UNION ROBIN *(NLD)*	83	1501	2310	78,6	12,1	4,2	10	gen
(ex Elisabeth S-95)								

Managing agents for:
Clyde Shipping Co Ltd bareboat chartered to **Barncrest Shipping Ltd**, Wadebridge

UNION SAINT ANGUS *(GBR)*	80	1082	1452	64,7	11,2	4,0	10	ro/gen
(ex Glenrosa-96, Saint Angus-94)								

THE UNITED KINGDOM GOVERNMENT

(Dept of Environment for Northern Ireland), 1 College Square East, Belfast, BT1 6DR

DIVIS II *(GBR)*	79	802	892	56,0	11,2	3,3	10	sludge

The **DIVIS II** approaches Belfast

(Alan Geddes)

UNITED MARINE DREDGERS LTD. (UMD)

Francis House, Shopwyke Road, Chichester, West Sussex, PO20 6AD (01243 817200/fax 01243 817216)

Managers for:
U.M.D. (Western) Ltd

CITY OF BRISTOL *(GBR)*		69	1092	1591	72,0	12,1	3,8	11	sd
(ex Hoveringham IV-90)									
CITY OF SOUTHAMPTON *(GBR)*		69	1092	1591	72,0	12,1	3,8	11	sd
(ex Hoveringham V-89)									

U.M.D. (Southern) Ltd

CITY OF CHICHESTER *(GBR)*		70	1056	1726	59,8	12,0	4,4	10	sd
(ex Chichester City-90)									
CITY OF PORTSMOUTH *(GBR)*		73	1046	1708	59,8	12,0	4,4	10	sd
(ex Chichester Star-90)									

U.M.D. (City of London) Ltd

CITY OF LONDON *(GBR)*		89	3660	5989	99,8	17,5	6,3	12	sd

U.M.D. (City of Westminster) Ltd

CITY OF WESTMINSTER *(GBR)*	90	3914	6604	99,9	17,7	6,7	12	sd
New buildings (Appledore)								
(Yd No.AS169)	Mar	97		2700			12	sd
(Yd No.AS170)	Jul	97		2700			12	sd

V SHIPS (UK) LTD.

Price Waterhouse Building, 30 Channel Way, Ocean Village, Southampton, SO14 3TG (01703 634477/ fax 01703 634319)

Managers for:
Cenargo International Ltd

New building 2 (Astilleros)	Mar	98	180,0		25 ro/px(150u)

See also MERCHANT FERRIES

THOMAS WATSON (SHIPPING) LTD.

252 High Street, Rochester, Kent, ME1 1HZ (01634 844632/4/fax 01634 831838)

Managers for:
Andrean Shipping Ltd

LADY ELSIE *(CYP)*		75	1031	1593	65,8	10,7	4,3	10	gen
(ex Canvey-92, Velox-88)									
LADY REA *(CYP)*		78	1954	3265	81,7	14,1	5,5	12	gen
(ex Ortrud-90, Carib Sun-88, Reggeland-87, Sylvia Delta-85)									

Ocean Wind Shipping Corp

LADY SANDRA *(BRB)*		72	1507	2230	76,5	12,1	4,6	11	gen
(ex Hendrik B-95, Ventura-94)									

Veneto Shipping Co Ltd

LADY SERENA *(CYP)*		95	2394	3697	87,8	12,3	5,4	11	gen(144c)
(ex Espero-96)									

Downlands Shipping Inc

LADY SOPHIA *(BHS)*		77	2208	4083	82,1	13,3	6,6	10	gen(32c)
(ex Enns-95, Norned Thor-84, Holberg-79, Atlantic Progress-77)									

Lakehead Shipping Ltd

LADY SYLVIA *(BHS)*		79	1707	2701	73,4	13,2	5,1	11	gen
(ex Inishfree—94, Arklow Vale-88, Capricorn-85)									

The **BALTIC TERN** leaves the locks at Holtenau and prepares to head westwards along the Kiel Canal   *(Dominic McCall)*

ANDREW WEIR SHIPPING LTD.

Dexter House, 2 Royal Mint Court, London, EC3N 4XX (0171 265-0808/fax 0171 816-4992)

BALTIC EAGLE *(IOM)*	79	14738	9450	137,1	26,0	8,2	18	ro(354c)
BALTIC EIDER *(IOM)*	89	20865	13866	157,7	25,3	8,5	19	ro(700c)
BALTIC TERN *(IOM)*	89	3896	3754	106,6	16,2	5,4	13	cc(316c)
CITY OF LISBON *(IOM)*	78	3992	4352	104,2	16,8	5,7	14	cc(300c)
(ex Cervantes-96, City of Plymouth-93)								
CITY OF MANCHESTER *(IOM)*	79	3992	4352	104,2	16,8	5,7	14	cc(300c)
(ex Laxfoss-85, City of Hartlepool-84)								
Chartered tonnage:								
Reederei m.s. "Cimbria" Harald Winter KG								
CHURRUCA *(ATG)*	91	3818	4650	103,5	16,2	6,1	14	gen(372c)
(ex Cimbria-93, Lloyd Iberia-92, Dana Sirena-91, launched as Cimbria)								
Ems-Fracht Schiffahrtges mbH & Co KG								
CALDERON *(ATG)*	96	3791	4750	99,8	16,5	5,9	15	gen(390c)
(ex Rheintal-96)								

WELLS MARINE SERVICES

Mill Garage, Maryland, Wells - next - the - Sea, Norfolk, NR23 1LX (01328 710117)

WALLBROOK *(GBR)*	40	244	310	39,6	7,7	3,0	8	sd

WEST OF SCOTLAND WATER

419 Balmore Road, Glasgow, G22 6NU (0141 842-5847/fax 0141 842-5850)

DALMARNOCK *(GBR)*	70	2182	3266	95,4	15,6	4,4	12	sludge
GARROCH HEAD *(GBR)*	77	2702	3671	98,7	16,0	4,4	11	sludge

THE WHITAKER GROUP

Crown Dry Dock, Tower Street, Hull, HU9 1TY (01482 320444/fax 01482 214850)
John H. Whitaker (Tankers) Ltd - Southern Division - Ocean Road Eastern Docks, Southampton, SO1 1AH
(01703 339989/fax 01703 339925)

John H. Whitaker (Holdings) Ltd								
WHITONIA *(GBR)* *	83	498	1180	50,0	9,5	4,0	9	gen
John H. Whitaker (Tankers) Ltd								
JAYNEE W *(GBR)*	96	1686	2750	75,0	12,5	4,9	12	bk tk
WHITASK *(GBR)*	78	640	844	57,3	10,9	2,9	10	tk
(ex Bromley-93)								
WHITCREST *(GBR)*	70	2144	3430	91,3	13,1	5,9	14	tk
(ex Esso Tenby-94)								
WHITIDE *(GBR)*	70	1148	2083	74,5	10,2	4,9	11	tk
(ex Lindvag-90, Tarnvik-78)								
WHITSEA *(GBR)*	71	728	1229	64,3	9,3	3,7	10	tk
(ex Bude-92)								
WHITSPRAY *(GBR)*	69	899	1321	64,6	11,1	3,4	10	tk
(ex Bristolian-93)								
WHITSTAR *(GBR)*	68	999	2140	74,3	10,2	4,8	11	bk tk
(ex Furena-91, Furenas-90, Stardex-79, Lone Wonsild)								
John H. Whitaker (Tankers) Ltd - Bristol Channel								
WHITHAVEN *(GBR)*	72	1204	1933	66,2	11,5	5,0	11	tk
(ex Frank C-94, Shell Director-93, Caernarvon-79)								
WHITANK *(GBR)*	76	686	1030	61,0	9,3	3,7	11	tk
(ex Luban-87)								
John H. Whitaker (Tankers) Ltd - Humber Area								
FARNDALE *(GBR)*	67	293	500	55,4	5,7	2,8	8	tk bge
(ex Farndale H-89)								
FOSSDALE H *(GBR)*	67	293	500	55,4	5,7	2,4	8	tk bge
FUSEDALE H *(GBR)*	68	293	500	55,4	5,7	2,4	8	tk bge
GROVEDALE *(GBR)*	66	364	570	50,3	6,6	3,4	8	tk bge
(ex Grovedale H-94)								
HUMBER ENDEAVOUR *(GBR)*	81	380	650	60,8	6,0	2,4	8	tk bge
(ex Fleet Endeavour-92)								
HUMBER ENERGY *(GBR)*	83	380	650	60,8	6,0	2,4	8	tk bge
HUMBER ENTERPRISE *(GBR)*	67	295	450	55,4	5,7	2,4	8	tk bge
HUMBER FUELLER *(GBR)*	57	192	300	43,8	5,5	2,4	7	tk bge
HUMBER JUBILEE *(GBR)*	77	382	650	60,9	6,0	2,7	9	tk bge
HUMBER PRIDE *(GBR)*	79	380	650	60,8	6,0	2,4	8	tk bge
HUMBER PRINCESS *(GBR)*	79	380	650	60,8	6,0	2,4	8	tk bge
HUMBER PROGRESS *(GBR)*	80	380	650	60,8	6,0	2,4	8	tk bge
HUMBER RENOWN *(GBR)*	67	295	500	55,4	5,7	2,4	8	tk bge
HUMBER STAR *(GBR)*	69	274	400	45,7	6,6	2,2	7	tk bge
(ex Wade Stone-77)								
John Harker Ltd - Mersey Area								
DEEPDALE H *(GBR)*	65	385	580	46,2	8,3	3,4	7	tk bge
(ex Riverbeacon-67)								
DOVEDALE H *(GBR)*	62	306	550	47,5	6,6	2,7	7	tk bge
(ex Riverbridge-67)								
HUMBER TRANSPORTER *(GBR)*	67	645	960	58,9	10,7	2,9	9	tk bge
(ex Shell Transporter-84, Poilo-79)								
WHARFDALE H *(GBR)*	60	609	1126	61,9	8,8	3,2	8	tk bge
WHITKIRK *(GBR)*	69	730	1219	64,6	9,2	3,7	10	tk
(ex Borman-89)								

John H. Whitaker (Tankers) Ltd - Southampton Area

Name (Flag)									
BATTLESTONE	(GBR)	68	293	500	55,4	5,7	2,4	9	tk bge
(ex Battlestone C- 89, Battle Stone-76)									
BORROWDALE H	(GBR)	72	385	550	50,6	6,7	3,1	8	tk bge
SOLENT RAIDER	(GBR)	68	605	1056	58,9	10,7	2,9	9	tk bge
(ex James Rayel-89, Vermion-84, Bebington-83, Pando-77)									
TEESDALE H	(GBR)	76	499	1050	43,9	10,0	3,9	8	tk
(ex Wilks-86)									

Note. * Laid up at Hull. See also R. LAPTHORN and FALMOUTH OIL SERVICES

The TEESDALE H, photographed off Hamble, was converted from a dry-cargo coaster to a bunkering tanker   *(Brian Ralfs)*

WILLIAMS SHIPPING MARINE LTD.

Berth 21, Ocean Road, Eastern Docks, Southampton, SO14 3GF (01703 237330/fax 01703 236151)

Name (Flag)									
MURIUS	(GBR)	62	125	213	29,8	6,2	2,0	7	gen bge

CHARLES M. WILLIE & CO. (SHIPPING) LTD.

Celtic House, Britannia Road, Roath Basin, Cardiff, CF1 5LS (01222 471000/fax 01222 471999)

Name (Flag)									
CELTIC NAVIGATOR	(BHS)	79	1010	1538	65,8	11,1	4,3	10	gen
(ex Wilant-89, Marant-88, Engel Klein-83)									
CELTIC VENTURE	(BHS)	71	1285	1533	79,0	11,1	4,1	12	gen(77c)
(ex Norman Commodore-91)									
CELTIC VOYAGER	(BHS)	75	1015	1519	65,7	10,8	4,1	10	gen
(ex Alannah Weston-84)									
CELTIC WARRIOR	(BHS)	91	3779	5878	92,8	17,1	6,6	13	gen(300c)
(ex Euro Merchant-95, Celtic Warrior-93)									

Name		Year							

CELTIC COMMANDER *(BHS)*   93   3840   5833   92,8   17,2   6,5   13   gen(361c)
(ex Fairway-96, Celtic Commander-94)
FAIRWIND *(BHS)*   94   3739   5788   92,8   17,2   6,5   13   gen(300c)
(ex Celtic Ambassador-94)
NENUFAR UNO *(ESP)*   92   3779   5861   92,8   17,1   6,6   13   gen(300c)
(ex Celtic Crusader-96, Euro Trader-95, Celtic Crusader-93)
Charles M. Willie Co (Investments) Ltd
GRACECHURCH
COMET *(BHS)* *   96   4015   6250   100,8   17,2   6,4   15   gen(467c)
(ex Celtic Sovereign-96)
GRACECHURCH SUN *(BHS)* *   95   4015   6250   100,0   17,0   6,4   15   gen(467c)
(ex Celtic Prince-96)
New buildings:
CELTIC MONARCH   97   3840   5900   100,0   17,0   6,4   15   gen(467c)
CELTIC PRINCESS   97   3840   5900   100,0   17,0   6,4   15   gen(467c)
Managers for:
   Iberian Seaways (Shipping) Ltd
IBERIAN COAST *(BHS)*   79   1029   1391   72,2   11,3   3,3   11   gen
(ex Yulence-87, London Miller-81)
IBERIAN OCEAN *(BHS)*   79   1029   1391   72,2   11,3   3,3   11   gen
(ex Zealence-87, Birkenhead Miller-82)
IBERIAN SEA *(BHS)*   88   2034   3366   85,1   13,0   6,0   11   gen
(launched as Ahmet Madenci II)
   Britamar
MAMORA *(BHS)* * *   75   926   1519   65,7   10,8   4,1   11   gen
(ex Celtic Mariner-90, Sarah Weston-84)
*Note.   * * Laid up Casablanca   * Chartered to* GRACECHURCH LINE *qv*

The CELTIC WARRIOR is seen in Birkenhead's West Float   *(Ambuscade Marine Photography)*

Owners/managers of the following vessels have not been fully identified

EILIDH OF KISHORN   + +   60   93   120   24,5   5,0   1,5   8   gen bge
(ex Needles-82)
PIBROCH *(GBR)*   + +   57   151   160   26,5   6,1   2,9   9   gen
GINO *(HND)* *   69   392   580   44,4   7,9   3,0   9   gen
(ex Ambience-82)
*Note.   + + Operating West Coast of Ireland   * Laid up Otterham Quay and under arrest - 31 Dec 96*

Abbreviations for vessel types

asp tk	asphalt tanker
bk tk	oil bunkering tanker
bk tk bge	oil bunkering tank barge
bulk	bulk carrier
cc(c)	container carrier (container capacity in Twenty foot Equivalent Units (TEUs))
cem	bulk cement carrier
ch tk	chemical tanker
drg/hpr	suction dredger/hopper
ed oil tk	edible oil tanker
ed oil bge	edible oil tank barge
eff tk	effluent tanker
eff tk bge	effluent tank barge
fish	vivier tank fish carrier
gen	general cargo
gen(c)	general cargo (container capacity in TEUs)
gen bge	general cargo barge
gen/pt	general cargo/palletised cargo
gen/ro	general cargo/RoRo facility on deck
gen/ro/ch	general cargo/RoRo facility on deck/chemicals in wing tanks
gen(sl)	general cargo/slurry
lpg	liquified gas tanker
lpg(ch)	liquified gas tanker - chlorine
l/v	livestock carrier
nuc	spent nuclear fuel carrier
oil/bit tk	oil/bitumen tanker
oil/ch/bit tk	oil/chemical/bitumen tanker
oil/ch tk	oil/chemical tanker
oil/veg tk	oil/vegetable oil tanker
ref	refrigerated cargo
ro(u)	RoRo cargo (capacity in12m trailer units - since increased to 13.6m)
ro h/l	RoRo heavy lift cargo
ro/px(u)	RoRo passenger (capacity in 12 m trailer units)
sand	sand and aggregate carrier
sd	sand/aggregate suction dredger
sludge	sludge carrier
tk	oil tanker
tk bge	oil tank barge
tk bge/gen	tank barge/general cargo
vc(v)	vehicle carrier (car capacity)
wt tk bge	potable water tank barge

Key to Flags

(AUT)	Austria	(HRV)	Croatia
(ATG)	Antigua & Barbuda	(IOM)	Isle of Man
(BHS)	Bahamas	(IRL)	Irish Republic
(BRB)	Barbados	(ITA)	Italy
(BMU)	Bermuda	(LBR)	Liberia
(CYM)	Cayman Islands	(MLT)	Malta
(CYP)	Cyprus	(NIS)	Norway (NIS)
(DEU)	Germany	(NLD)	Netherlands
(DIS)	Denmark(DIS)	(PAN)	Panama
(ESP)	Spain	(POL)	Poland
(FIN)	Finland	(VCT)	St Vincent & the Grenadines
(GIB)	Gibraltar	(VUT)	Vanuatu
(HKG)	Hong Kong	(TUV)	Tuvalu
(HND)	Honduras		

SHIP NAME INDEX

ELIZA PG	11	GREENDALE H	19	K/TOULSON	14
ELIZABETH C	12	GRETA C	12	KASLA	4
ELLEN W	28	GRETE THERESA	29	KATHERINE BORCHARD	27
ELK	46	GROVEDALE	63	KELLS	24
EMERALD	56	GRY MARITHA	32	KENMARE (2435/68)	18
EMILY C	12			KENMARE (5306/75)	24
EMILY PG	11			KILLARNEY	25
EMMA	20	HAAHR X...	42	KINDRENCE	15
EMSLAND	31	HARCUSS	58	KINSALE	25
ENDEAVOUR	22	HARMA	30	KIRSTEN	13
ERIC HAMMANN	34	HARTING	56	KISH	4
ESTIRENO	47	HAWESWATER	19	KLAZINA C	12
ETTRICK	26	HEEREPLEIN	52	KORALLE	31
EURO POWER	20	HELEEN C	12	KRISTIANNE ELISA	16
EUROPEAN		HELMSDALE	30	KYLEMORE	25
SHEARWATER	23	HERA	55		
EUROPEAN X...	45	HERM J	13	LADY X...	61
EVERT PRAHM	34	HERNES	32	LANCING	56
EXCALIBUR	22	HEYO PRAHM	34	LANCRESSE	4
		HIGHLAND	16	LANRICK	26
FAIRWIND	65	HOHEBANK	31	LENNARD	5
FALMOUTH X...	22	HOLM SOUND	48	LEOPARD	44
FARNDALE	63	HOO...	33	LESZEK G	51
FAST KEN	33	HOO X...	33	LION	44
FINN VALLEY OIL	22	HOOK SAND	33	LINDA BUCK	52
FIONA MAY	43	HOPE	56	LIZRIX	49
FLEUR-DE-LYS	18	HORDNES	32	LOCATOR	47
FORTH BRIDGE	11	HOUNSLOW	16	LODELLA	47
FORTH FISHER	23	HUELIN DISPATCH	30	LOFTEN	8
FOSSDALE H	63	HULL PARAGON	25	LORD CITRINE	32
FOSSELAND	57	HUMBER X...	63	LORD HINTON	32
FREDERICK M	24	HUMBER MARINER	13	LORE PRAHM	34
FULFORD	14	HUMBER MONARCH	17	LOUISA GRACE	27
FURNESS FISHER	23	HUSNES	32	LUBCHEM	56
FUSEDALE H	63			LUCY PG	11
				LUMINENCE	15
		IBERIAN X...	65	LYRAWA BAY	8
G.D.DISTRIBUTOR	47	IBEX	44		
GABRIELE WEHR	45	ILONA G	33		
GAMMAGAS	53	INGA	31	MAERSK X...	42
GARDEN	6	INISH...	7	MAGRIX	49
GARDYLOO	19	INZHENER	42	MAMORA	65
GARROCH HEAD	62	IRISHGATE	23	MARINE EVANGELINE	50
GEM	56	ISIS	4	MARK C	12
GEORGE ODEY	17	ISLAND COMMODORE	13	MARK PRIOR	47
GERARD PATRICK		ISLE OF TIREE	29	MARLENE GRACE	27
PURCELL	54			MARPOL	14
GERHARD PRAHM	34			MARTHA HAMMANN	34
GERINA	58	JAMES PRIOR	47	MARY C	12
GERLENA	59	JAN BECKER	9	MATHILDA	50
GILBERT J. FOWLER	43	JANE	14	MATRISHA	11
GINO	65	JAYNEE W	63	MAUREEN ANN	17
GOLDCREST	16	JEVINGTON	56	MB X...	3
GOOLE STAR	14	JOHN ADAMS	28	MEDINA RIVER	43
GRACECHURCH COMET	65	JOHNO	57	MEDWAY	49
GRACECHURCH SUN	65	JOLLY MINER	17	MERCHANT X...	40
GRACECHURCH X...	27	JONRIX	49	MERLE	8
GREEBA RIVER	41	JORUND	52	MICHAEL ANE	42

J. & A. Gardner & Co. Ltd.

—

Shipowners, Ships Agents, Ships Managers
and Quarry Masters

—

**16 ROBERTSON STREET
GLASGOW
G2 8DU**

TELEPHONE: 0141 221 7845
FACSIMILE: 0141 204 2388
TELEX: 77205